ILLUMINATE PRAYER JOURNAL

CJ and Shelley Hitz

This Journal
Belongs to :

_____

Your word is a lamp to guide my feet
and a light for my path.

— PSALM 119:105

CONTENTS

Prayer

Illuminate.

What comes to your mind when you hear this word? Perhaps a morning sunrise that gradually brings more illumination with each passing minute. Or a flash of lightning in the darkness that illuminates the landscape for a split second. Maybe a Christmas Eve service where the sanctuary is illuminated with each candle that is lit.

Shelley and I both enjoy running. As a runner, there are times when wearing a headlamp is necessary, especially when running in the dark on technical, undulating trails. Headlamps vary in the number of lumens or brightness they project. More lumens mean more visibility. Having the ability to see just 50-75 feet down the trail can be the difference between staying upright or falling on your face as you trip over a rock or root.

Psalm 119:105 says, *"Your word is a lamp to guide my feet and a light for my path."*

The Hebrew word for "light" in this verse is *Owr* (pronounced like "or"). One of the meanings of this little word is illumination. God's Word is like a headlamp giving us light for the path ahead.

Another important aspect of headlamps is the necessity of replacing the batteries. As the battery life begins to fade, the brightness of the headlamp will slowly grow dim. This can make each step more and more treacherous, especially on unfamiliar trails.

Prayer = Power

When we spend time with our Heavenly Father in prayer, we are allowing Him to recharge our batteries—spirit, soul, and body—which illuminates His Word that much more. When we connect with the Father, we are connecting with our eternal Power Source. Jesus knew the power of connecting with His Abba (Hebrew word for "Daddy") Father. We read in Luke 5:16 that "Jesus often withdrew to the wilderness for prayer."

If the Son of God knew the importance of withdrawing "often" for prayer, how about you and me? All we have to do is look at the fruit of Jesus' life. The "proof is in the pudding" as they say. And how intimately connected was Jesus to his Father?

"I tell you the truth, the Son can do nothing by himself. He does only what he sees the Father doing. Whatever the Father does, the Son also does." (John 5:19)

The Son can do nothing by Himself.

Let that sink in for a few seconds. When we pause to spend time in prayer, we're acknowledging our dire need to receive God's power and direction for our lives. Like oxygen for the body, deep connection with our Creator is what our souls long for.

On my own, my batteries quickly fade. This becomes treacherous when trying to navigate the darkness of this world. Connected to the Father, my path ahead is illuminated and I'm able to help others who may be running alongside me.

It is our hope that God uses the *Illuminate Prayer Journal* to deepen your relationship with Him while also stirring up a hunger for His Word in Scripture. Whether you spend ten minutes or an hour with the Lord each day, it's more about the quality of the time you spend rather than the quantity. May our lives become more illuminated with each passing day!

"You are the light of the world—like a city on a hilltop that cannot be hidden. No one lights a lamp and then puts it under a basket. Instead, a lamp is placed on a stand, where it gives light to everyone in the house." (Matthew 5:14-15)

CHAPTER ONE

HOW TO USE THIS JOURNAL

To be honest, CJ and I created this journal for ourselves. It came out of a desire to be more intentional in our prayer times each day.

Let's be real.

It's easy to say a few token words in prayer and then get distracted by our phones, our to-do lists and/or other people and never go deeper in prayer with God.

Every day we are bombarded with messages through email, social media, TV, etc. It is easy to get weighed down by the cares of this world.

This journal will help you to stay focused in your prayer time and create space to hear from God.

How to Hear God's Voice

One of the most life-changing moments for me was when I, Shelley, learned how to hear God's voice. I attended a workshop by Mark Virkler in 2009 and my life has never been the same.

I highly recommend his book and teaching materials, *How to Hear God's Voice*. In fact, I purchased the rights to teach his materials and you can watch the training for free as a bonus to this book, a $69 value.

Sign up for the "How to Hear God's Voice" workshop here: www.yourcreativeadventure.com/illuminatebonus

Getting Started

This thirty-day journal has no dates so you can start and stop at any time.

If you miss a few days, simply pick up where you left off. I encourage you to let go of any legalistic ideas such as, "I need to meet with God perfectly every day in order to be accepted by Him."

If you have a relationship with Jesus, you are now a son or daughter of God. You are loved, accepted and validated for who you are, not for what you do. I encourage you to rest in His love for you and find your identity in Him. Let go of the need to perform or to do things for God.

Yes, God longs for a relationship with you. But not out of duty or obligation.

Therefore, I encourage you to be free when using this journal and not to get caught up in the need to spend time with God in a "certain" way.

Intimacy with God is the most important goal. Whatever that looks like for you, you're doing it right!

Your Environment

Personally, I like to have my time with the Lord in the same place every day. Sometimes I will diffuse essential oils or light a candle.

Almost every day I play soft instrumental music in the background. I recommend Tammy Sorenson's music. You can find it on iTunes, Spotify, and her website here: http://tammysorenson.com.

Get Creative

Integrating creativity and color within your journal is recommended but not required. You can get started with a pen or pencil. However, you can use pens with different colors. As an artist, I use the Sakura Pigma Micron fine line pen set with assorted colors. You can find these pens at your local art store or online at Amazon.

You can also add creative hand lettering to your journal.

I will typically add lettering using the Tombow fudenosuke hard pen or the Zebra superfine brush pen in the sections for Bible reading and writing out a godly affirmation.

I have tested these pens and none of them bleed through the paper for me. However, I recommend testing your pens first in the back of your journal before you start using them every day.

You can also use faux calligraphy (fake calligraphy) which uses your hand writing and allows you to get started right away. Sign up for my free class that teaches you three simple steps to get started with hand lettering here: www.yourcreativeadventure.com/free

Weekly Journaling

Each week includes three pages to help you go deeper in prayer. There is a page to write out your weekly prayer requests. Then there are two pages for journaling about the vision God has for your life. You will review the picture God gives you each day in your journal.

If this is a new concept for you, I encourage you to review the video on vision in the bonus training that comes with this book. Sign up here: www.yourcreativeadventure.com/illuminatebonus

For each day in the journal is a section to pray for one of your specific weekly prayer requests.

I encourage you to go back and mark when your weekly prayer requests have been answered. This increases your faith and encourages you to keep praying and interceding for others.

Walkthrough of Each Section

1. Silent Meditation

The *Illuminate Prayer Journal* starts with five minutes of silent meditation. You can repeat a breath prayer over and over like, "Come, Lord Jesus" and you can play soft instrumental music during this time if you want.

Research has shown over and over the power of silence in our lives. We don't get enough of it in our fast-paced, social media world. Therefore, starting with a few minutes of silent meditation is powerful.

To learn more about this, listen to episode 200 of the Revelation Wellness podcast.

2. Gratitude

Each day you will write out three things you are grateful for in the last twenty-four hours. If possible, write something specific. Otherwise, it is easy to write out general things like, "family, friends, and health" over and over.

However, what specific trait are you grateful for in your spouse today? Or what did your friend do for you yesterday that was a blessing? In what ways did God provide for you in the last twenty-four hours?

Gratitude changes us as we put our focus on the specific things we are grateful for each day.

3. Confession

Now it's time to clear the air with God and confess any sin from the last twenty-four hours.

Confession isn't a one-time event. Instead, it's an ongoing cleansing. First John 1:9 says, "But if we confess our sins to him, he is faithful and just to forgive us our sins and to cleanse us from all wickedness."

Imagine if you decided not to shower for a month. No one would probably want to sit next to you at church, right?

Body odor and greasy hair are just a few signs that you have not been cleansing your physical body each day.

The same is true for us spiritually. When we go long periods of time without confessing our sin to God, people will begin to notice.

For example, we might have less patience with our family. Or we might get frustrated and complain more often.

It may just take a moment, but take the time to confess your specific sins from the last day.

When I started using the *Illuminate Prayer Journal* and intentionally confessing my sin each day, I started to see trends.

This helped me recognize areas I still need to grow in spiritually and emotionally. I was then able to bring these areas to the Lord during my listening prayer time and receive His guidance and help.

4. Invite the Holy Spirit

Invite the Holy Spirit to teach you from the Scriptures each day. You can use the prayer we've written out for you.

Holy Spirit come and open my mind so I can understand and receive what You have for me in Your Word. Reveal Yourself to me.

"Then he opened their minds to understand the Scriptures." (Luke 24:45).

"But when the Father sends the Advocate as my representative—that is, the Holy Spirit—he will teach you everything and will remind you of everything I have told you." (John 14:26).

5. Bible Reading

Now it's time to read God's Word. You can choose to read and meditate on one verse or read several chapters.

Lately, I have been using a one-year reading plan. It usually takes me longer than one year to finish the plan, but God always reminds me that there is freedom and grace.

Plus, it seems like whatever I'm reading that day is exactly what I needed. Right on time!

Take the time to write out at least one takeaway from your Bible reading for the day. This is a great place to get colorful and creative in your journal.

6. Write Out Your Prayers.

In this section, start off by writing everything that is currently on your heart and mind in this section.

Pour out your heart to God (Psalms 62:8) and allow Him to clear your mind of the clutter. This will create space for you to hear God's still small voice (1 Kings 19:12) as you continue to journal in the next section.

7. Listening Prayer (two-way journaling).

This is a conversation between you and God. Start off by asking an open-ended question in your journal. Then wait to hear God's voice and write what you sense Him saying to you. See the appendix for sample questions.

As you write out what you sense God saying, you may find it helpful to write in a different color or put an arrow next to that section to easily see where the conversation changes.

Again, if this is new to you, I highly recommend taking our free workshop on "How to Hear God's Voice." It is included as a bonus to this book. Get access here: www.yourcreativeadventure.com/illuminatebonus

We have also included extra journaling pages at the back of the book when you want to go deeper or have more to say.

8. Review the Vision God has Given You

This is where you will review the vision God gave you for your life, business, etc. at the beginning of the week. Close your eyes, see it in your mind like a video and feel the emotions it brings. Write a summary of what you see.

You can also use this time to set an intention for your day. Visualize what God has for you based on His Word and feel the emotion of it.

This is a great way to start your day.

9. Godly Affirmation

Write out or letter one godly affirmation based on Scripture that you need to hear each day. For example, I am loved.

In the appendix, we have a list of godly affirmations for you to use in the appendix, but we encourage you to come up with your own as well.

This is another great place to add color and creativity to your journal.

10. Weekly Prayer Requests

Pray for one of your weekly prayer requests. Refer back to the list you wrote at the beginning of the week. Choose one request and pray specifically for that person or request.

11. Gratitude, Praise and Worship

End your prayer time in gratitude, praise, and worship. Thank God for hearing your prayers and for anything else that comes to mind. Praise Him for what He has done for you and worship Him alone. As you worship, put your full focus on God and not on yourself.

Thanksgiving is a gate opener and praise brings us into God's presence (Psalm 100:4). Worship puts the focus on God. He is the main character of our story, not us!

Video Example

As a visual person myself, I know how helpful it can be to see an example on video. Therefore, I recorded a video for you showing a sample journaling session and how I use each section. Watch the video here: www.yourcreativeadventure.com/illuminatejournalvideo

Let's Get Started!

As I mentioned previously, use this journal in the way that is most life-giving to you. Skip sections on certain days if you want.

The focus of this journal is to create time to connect with God and have intimacy with Him.

Please know that we are praying for each one of you. We pray that as you use this journal God will lead you to hear His voice and that He will draw you closer to Himself.

We are on this journey together!

Prayer IS THE

proof WE ARE

relying ON

God

- CJ HITZ

Weekly Prayer Requests

Date:_____

family:

Date answered: _____

_____

_____

_____

friends:

Date answered: _____

_____

_____

_____

the world:

Date answered: _____

_____

_____

_____

myself:

Date answered: _____

_____

_____

_____

other:

Date answered: _____

_____

_____

_____

Once a week, spend time asking God for His vision for your life, business, etc. Proverbs 29:18 says, "Without vision, we perish" (KJV).

1. God, show me your vision for: _____
   (my life, my business, my marriage).
2. Ask God for a picture. See yourself in the vision God has for you. Close your eyes and visualize. Write out or sketch what you see below.
3. What will it feel like? Ask God for an emotion to attach to the vision He has for you. This is powerful! Write about it below.

God, show me your vision for:

☐ Thank God for what He showed you below. Then ask Him, "Lord, is there more?

Close your eyes and look for more in the picture God gave you. Write out or sketch what you see below.

Lord, is there more?

Date: _____

☐ Start with five minutes in silent meditation or with a breath prayer. See the appendix for examples.

☐ Begin with gratitude. Write out three things you are grateful for today. Be specific and include anything that happened in the last twenty-four hours.

Thank you, God, for: _____

Thank you, God, for: _____

Thank you, God, for: _____

☐ Take a moment to confess any sin from the last twenty-four hours and ask for God's forgiveness. _____

_____

_____

☐ Invite the Holy Spirit to teach you from the Scriptures today. *Holy Spirit come and open my mind so I can understand and receive what You have for me in Your Word. Reveal Yourself to me.*

☐ Bible reading. Write one takeaway from the verses you read today. If you prefer, choose a phrase that stuck out to you and write it out or letter it below.

☐ Write out your prayers. Start off by writing everything that is currently on your heart and mind below. Pour out your heart to God (Psalms 62:8) and allow Him to clear your mind of the clutter. This will create space for you to hear God's still small voice (1 Kings 19:12) as you continue to journal on the next page.

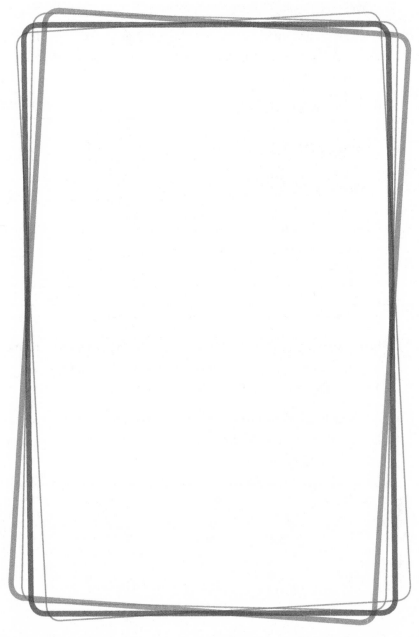

☐ Listening prayer (two-way journaling). This is a conversation between you and God. Start off by asking an open ended question in your journal below. Then wait to hear God's voice and write what you sense Him saying to you. See the appendix for sample questions.

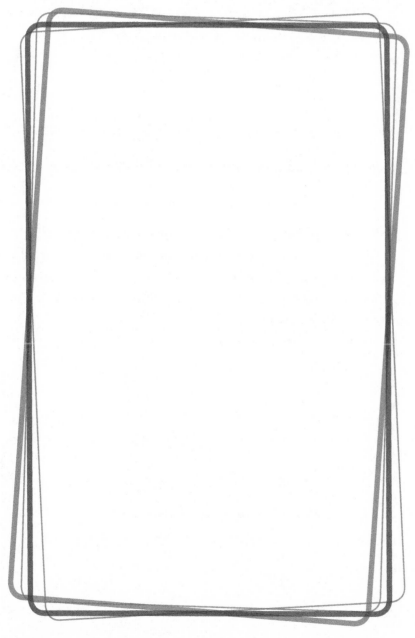

☐ Review the vision God has given you for your life, business, family, etc. Close your eyes, see it in your mind like a video and feel the emotions it brings. Write a summary here:

_____

☐ Write out or letter one godly affirmation below based on Scripture that you need to hear today. For example, I am loved.

☐ Pray for one of your weekly prayer requests. Write it here:

_____

☐ End your prayer time in gratitude, praise, and worship. Thank God for hearing your prayers and for anything else that comes to mind. Praise Him for what He has done for you and worship Him alone. As you worship, put your full focus on God and not on yourself.

Gratitude:

Praise:

Worship:

Date: _____

⚬⚬⚬

☐ Start with five minutes in silent meditation or with a breath prayer. See the appendix for examples.

☐ Begin with gratitude. Write out three things you are grateful for today. Be specific and include anything that happened in the last twenty-four hours.

Thank you, God, for: _____

Thank you, God, for: _____

Thank you, God, for: _____

☐ Take a moment to confess any sin from the last twenty-four hours and ask for God's forgiveness. _____

_____

_____

☐ Invite the Holy Spirit to teach you from the Scriptures today. *Holy Spirit come and open my mind so I can understand and receive what You have for me in Your Word. Reveal Yourself to me.*

☐ Bible reading. Write one takeaway from the verses you read today. If you prefer, choose a phrase that stuck out to you and write it out or letter it below.

Write out your prayers. Start off by writing everything that is currently on your heart and mind below. Pour out your heart to God (Psalms 62:8) and allow Him to clear your mind of the clutter. This will create space for you to hear God's still small voice (1 Kings 19:12) as you continue to journal on the next page.

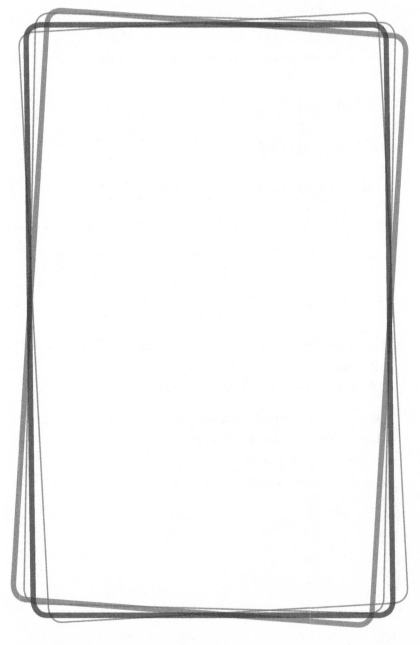

☐ Listening prayer (two-way journaling). This is a conversation between you and God. Start off by asking an open ended question in your journal below. Then wait to hear God's voice and write what you sense Him saying to you. See the appendix for sample questions.

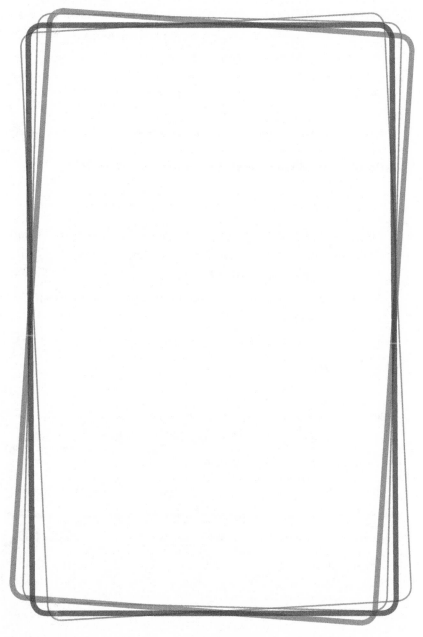

☐ Review the vision God has given you for your life, business, family, etc. Close your eyes, see it in your mind like a video and feel the emotions it brings. Write a summary here:

_____

☐ Write out or letter one godly affirmation below based on Scripture that you need to hear today. For example, I am loved.

☐ Pray for one of your weekly prayer requests. Write it here:

_____

☐ End your prayer time in gratitude, praise, and worship. Thank God for hearing your prayers and for anything else that comes to mind. Praise Him for what He has done for you and worship Him alone. As you worship, put your full focus on God and not on yourself.

Gratitude:

Praise:

Worship:

Date: _____

Start with five minutes in silent meditation or with a breath prayer. See the appendix for examples.

Begin with gratitude. Write out three things you are grateful for today. Be specific and include anything that happened in the last twenty-four hours.

Thank you, God, for: _____

Thank you, God, for: _____

Thank you, God, for: _____

Take a moment to confess any sin from the last twenty-four hours and ask for God's forgiveness. _____

_____

_____

Invite the Holy Spirit to teach you from the Scriptures today. *Holy Spirit come and open my mind so I can understand and receive what You have for me in Your Word. Reveal Yourself to me.*

Bible reading. Write one takeaway from the verses you read today. If you prefer, choose a phrase that stuck out to you and write it out or letter it below.

Write out your prayers. Start off by writing everything that is currently on your heart and mind below. Pour out your heart to God (Psalms 62:8) and allow Him to clear your mind of the clutter. This will create space for you to hear God's still small voice (1 Kings 19:12) as you continue to journal on the next page.

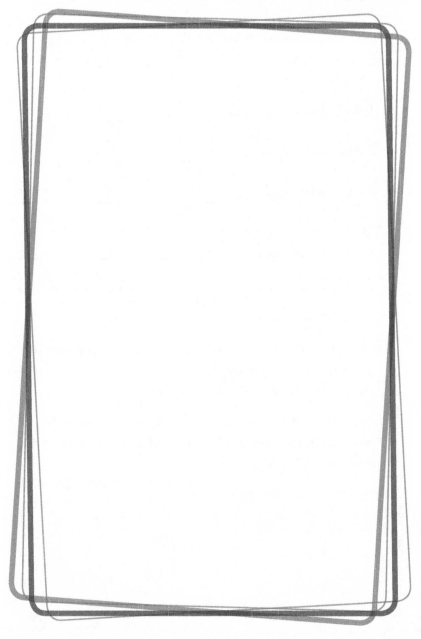

Listening prayer (two-way journaling). This is a conversation between you and God. Start off by asking an open ended question in your journal below. Then wait to hear God's voice and write what you sense Him saying to you. See the appendix for sample questions.

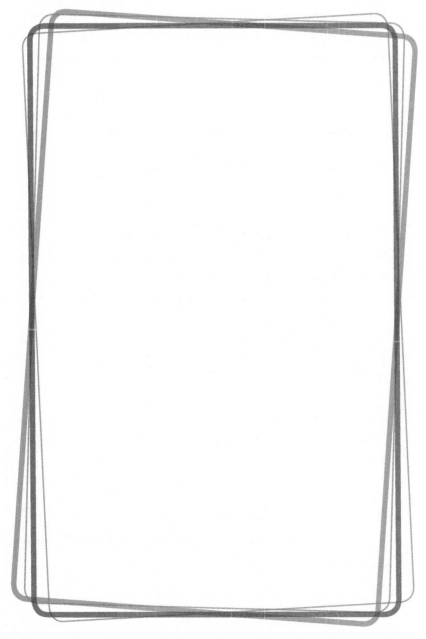

☐ Review the vision God has given you for your life, business, family, etc. Close your eyes, see it in your mind like a video and feel the emotions it brings. Write a summary here:

_____

☐ Write out or letter one godly affirmation below based on Scripture that you need to hear today. For example, I am loved.

☐ Pray for one of your weekly prayer requests. Write it here:

_____

☐ End your prayer time in gratitude, praise, and worship. Thank God for hearing your prayers and for anything else that comes to mind. Praise Him for what He has done for you and worship Him alone. As you worship, put your full focus on God and not on yourself.

Gratitude:

Praise:

Worship:

Date: _____

☐ Start with five minutes in silent meditation or with a breath prayer. See the appendix for examples.

☐ Begin with gratitude. Write out three things you are grateful for today. Be specific and include anything that happened in the last twenty-four hours.

Thank you, God, for: _____

Thank you, God, for: _____

Thank you, God, for: _____

☐ Take a moment to confess any sin from the last twenty-four hours and ask for God's forgiveness. _____

_____

_____

☐ Invite the Holy Spirit to teach you from the Scriptures today. *Holy Spirit come and open my mind so I can understand and receive what You have for me in Your Word. Reveal Yourself to me.*

☐ Bible reading. Write one takeaway from the verses you read today. If you prefer, choose a phrase that stuck out to you and write it out or letter it below.

Write out your prayers. Start off by writing everything that is currently on your heart and mind below. Pour out your heart to God (Psalms 62:8) and allow Him to clear your mind of the clutter. This will create space for you to hear God's still small voice (1 Kings 19:12) as you continue to journal on the next page.

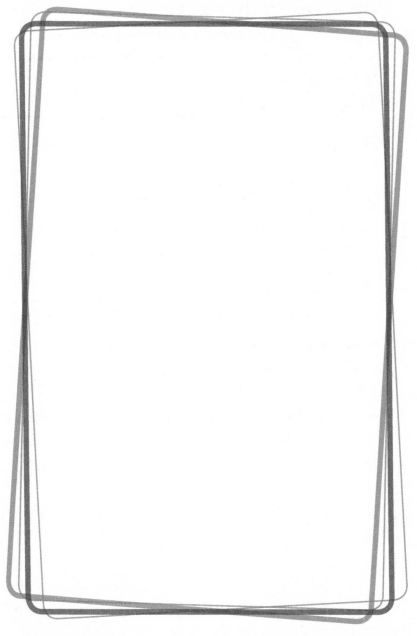

Listening prayer (two-way journaling). This is a conversation between you and God. Start off by asking an open ended question in your journal below. Then wait to hear God's voice and write what you sense Him saying to you. See the appendix for sample questions.

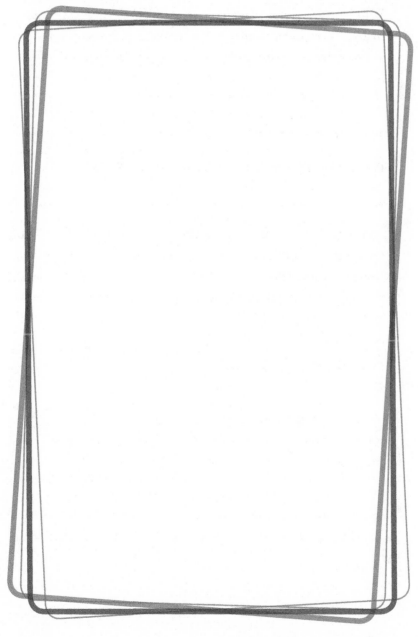

☐ Review the vision God has given you for your life, business, family, etc. Close your eyes, see it in your mind like a video and feel the emotions it brings. Write a summary here:

_____

☐ Write out or letter one godly affirmation below based on Scripture that you need to hear today. For example, I am loved.

☐ Pray for one of your weekly prayer requests. Write it here:

_____

☐ End your prayer time in gratitude, praise, and worship. Thank God for hearing your prayers and for anything else that comes to mind. Praise Him for what He has done for you and worship Him alone. As you worship, put your full focus on God and not on yourself.

Gratitude:

Praise:

Worship:

Date: _____

⎯⎯ ⌁ ⎯⎯

☐ Start with five minutes in silent meditation or with a breath prayer. See the appendix for examples.

☐ Begin with gratitude. Write out three things you are grateful for today. Be specific and include anything that happened in the last twenty-four hours.

Thank you, God, for: _____

Thank you, God, for: _____

Thank you, God, for: _____

☐ Take a moment to confess any sin from the last twenty-four hours and ask for God's forgiveness. _____

_____

_____

☐ Invite the Holy Spirit to teach you from the Scriptures today. *Holy Spirit come and open my mind so I can understand and receive what You have for me in Your Word. Reveal Yourself to me.*

☐ Bible reading. Write one takeaway from the verses you read today. If you prefer, choose a phrase that stuck out to you and write it out or letter it below.

Write out your prayers. Start off by writing everything that is currently on your heart and mind below. Pour out your heart to God (Psalms 62:8) and allow Him to clear your mind of the clutter. This will create space for you to hear God's still small voice (1 Kings 19:12) as you continue to journal on the next page.

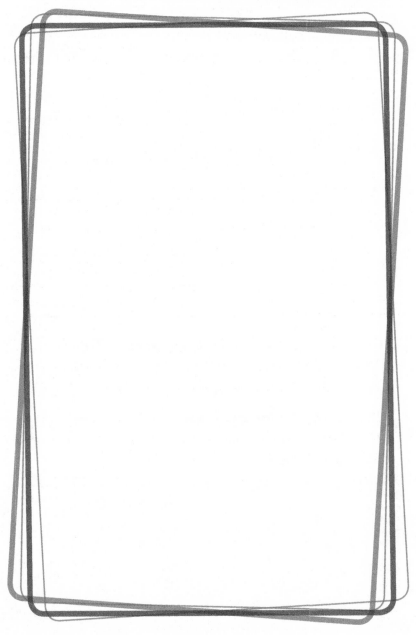

☐ Listening prayer (two-way journaling). This is a conversation between you and God. Start off by asking an open ended question in your journal below. Then wait to hear God's voice and write what you sense Him saying to you. See the appendix for sample questions.

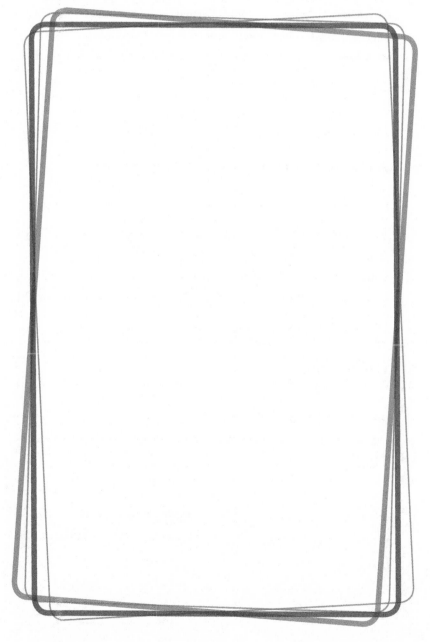

☐ Review the vision God has given you for your life, business, family, etc. Close your eyes, see it in your mind like a video and feel the emotions it brings. Write a summary here:

_____

☐ Write out or letter one godly affirmation below based on Scripture that you need to hear today. For example, I am loved.

_____

☐ Pray for one of your weekly prayer requests. Write it here:

_____

☐ End your prayer time in gratitude, praise, and worship. Thank God for hearing your prayers and for anything else that comes to mind. Praise Him for what He has done for you and worship Him alone. As you worship, put your full focus on God and not on yourself.

Gratitude:

Praise:

Worship:

Date: _____

☐ Start with five minutes in silent meditation or with a breath prayer. See the appendix for examples.

☐ Begin with gratitude. Write out three things you are grateful for today. Be specific and include anything that happened in the last twenty-four hours.

Thank you, God, for: _____

Thank you, God, for: _____

Thank you, God, for: _____

☐ Take a moment to confess any sin from the last twenty-four hours and ask for God's forgiveness. _____

_____

_____

☐ Invite the Holy Spirit to teach you from the Scriptures today. *Holy Spirit come and open my mind so I can understand and receive what You have for me in Your Word. Reveal Yourself to me.*

☐ Bible reading. Write one takeaway from the verses you read today. If you prefer, choose a phrase that stuck out to you and write it out or letter it below.

☐ Write out your prayers. Start off by writing everything that is currently on your heart and mind below. Pour out your heart to God (Psalms 62:8) and allow Him to clear your mind of the clutter. This will create space for you to hear God's still small voice (1 Kings 19:12) as you continue to journal on the next page.

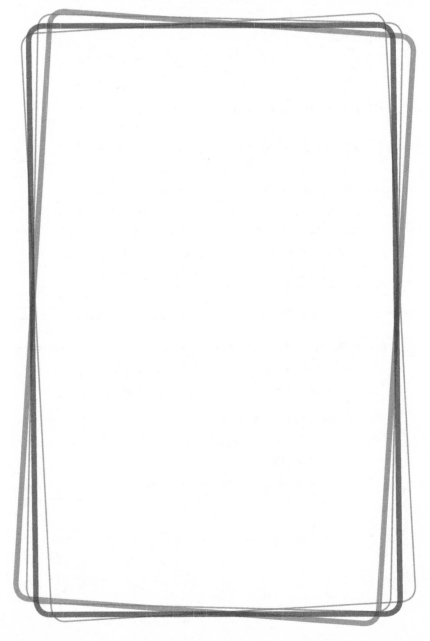

☐ Listening prayer (two-way journaling). This is a conversation between you and God. Start off by asking an open ended question in your journal below. Then wait to hear God's voice and write what you sense Him saying to you. See the appendix for sample questions.

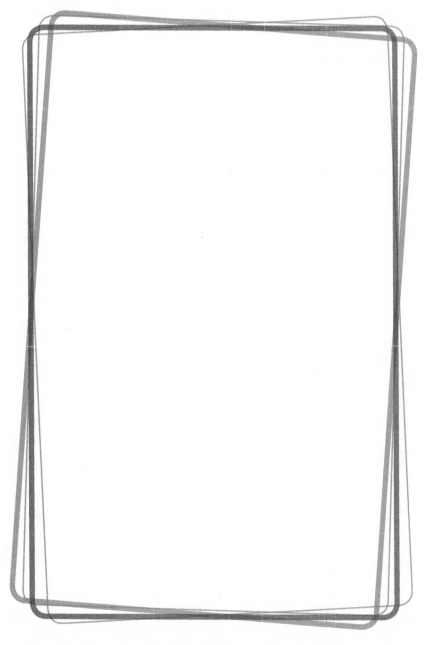

☐ Review the vision God has given you for your life, business, family, etc. Close your eyes, see it in your mind like a video and feel the emotions it brings. Write a summary here:

_____

☐ Write out or letter one godly affirmation below based on Scripture that you need to hear today. For example, I am loved.

☐ Pray for one of your weekly prayer requests. Write it here:

_____

☐ End your prayer time in gratitude, praise, and worship. Thank God for hearing your prayers and for anything else that comes to mind. Praise Him for what He has done for you and worship Him alone. As you worship, put your full focus on God and not on yourself.

Gratitude:

Praise:

Worship:

Date: _____

☐ Start with five minutes in silent meditation or with a breath prayer. See the appendix for examples.

☐ Begin with gratitude. Write out three things you are grateful for today. Be specific and include anything that happened in the last twenty-four hours.

Thank you, God, for: _____

Thank you, God, for: _____

Thank you, God, for: _____

☐ Take a moment to confess any sin from the last twenty-four hours and ask for God's forgiveness. _____

_____

_____

☐ Invite the Holy Spirit to teach you from the Scriptures today. *Holy Spirit come and open my mind so I can understand and receive what You have for me in Your Word. Reveal Yourself to me.*

☐ Bible reading. Write one takeaway from the verses you read today. If you prefer, choose a phrase that stuck out to you and write it out or letter it below.

Write out your prayers. Start off by writing everything that is currently on your heart and mind below. Pour out your heart to God (Psalms 62:8) and allow Him to clear your mind of the clutter. This will create space for you to hear God's still small voice (1 Kings 19:12) as you continue to journal on the next page.

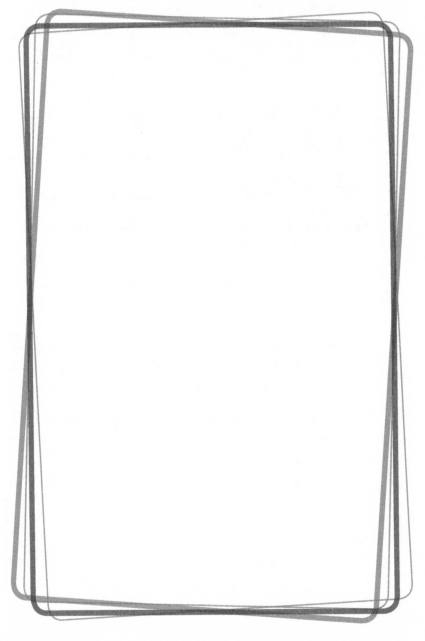

☐ Listening prayer (two-way journaling). This is a conversation between you and God. Start off by asking an open ended question in your journal below. Then wait to hear God's voice and write what you sense Him saying to you. See the appendix for sample questions.

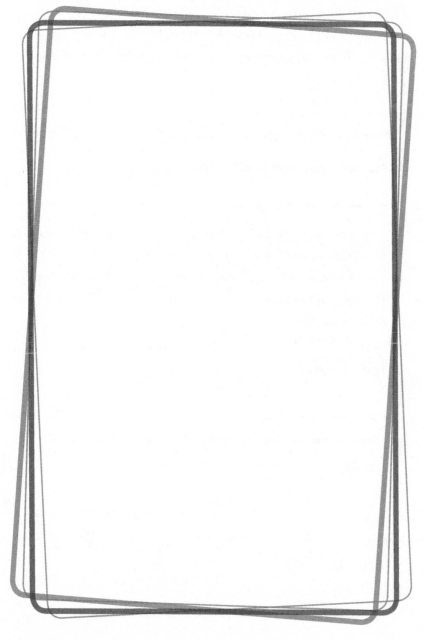

☐ Review the vision God has given you for your life, business, family, etc. Close your eyes, see it in your mind like a video and feel the emotions it brings. Write a summary here:

_____

☐ Write out or letter one godly affirmation below based on Scripture that you need to hear today. For example, I am loved.

☐ Pray for one of your weekly prayer requests. Write it here:

_____

☐ End your prayer time in gratitude, praise, and worship. Thank God for hearing your prayers and for anything else that comes to mind. Praise Him for what He has done for you and worship Him alone. As you worship, put your full focus on God and not on yourself.

Gratitude:

Praise:

Worship:

Never stop Praying

1 THESSALONIANS 5:17

Weekly Prayer Requests

Date: _____

family:

Date answered: _____

_____

_____

_____

friends:

Date answered: _____

_____

_____

_____

the world:

Date answered: _____

_____

_____

_____

myself:

Date answered: _____

_____

_____

_____

other:

Date answered: _____

_____

_____

_____

☐ Once a week, spend time asking God for His vision for your life, business, etc. Proverbs 29:18 says, "Without vision, we perish" (KJV).

1. God, show me your vision for: _____
   (my life, my business, my marriage).
2. Ask God for a picture. See yourself in the vision God has for you. Close your eyes and visualize. Write out or sketch what you see below.
3. What will it feel like? Ask God for an emotion to attach to the vision He has for you. This is powerful! Write about it below.

God, show me your vision for:

☐ Thank God for what He showed you below. Then ask Him, "Lord, is there more?

Close your eyes and look for more in the picture God gave you. Write out or sketch what you see below.

Lord, is there more?

Date: _____

- [ ] Start with five minutes in silent meditation or with a breath prayer. See the appendix for examples.

- [ ] Begin with gratitude. Write out three things you are grateful for today. Be specific and include anything that happened in the last twenty-four hours.

Thank you, God, for: _____

Thank you, God, for: _____

Thank you, God, for: _____

- [ ] Take a moment to confess any sin from the last twenty-four hours and ask for God's forgiveness. _____

  _____

  _____

- [ ] Invite the Holy Spirit to teach you from the Scriptures today. *Holy Spirit come and open my mind so I can understand and receive what You have for me in Your Word. Reveal Yourself to me.*

- [ ] Bible reading. Write one takeaway from the verses you read today. If you prefer, choose a phrase that stuck out to you and write it out or letter it below.

Write out your prayers. Start off by writing everything that is currently on your heart and mind below. Pour out your heart to God (Psalms 62:8) and allow Him to clear your mind of the clutter. This will create space for you to hear God's still small voice (1 Kings 19:12) as you continue to journal on the next page.

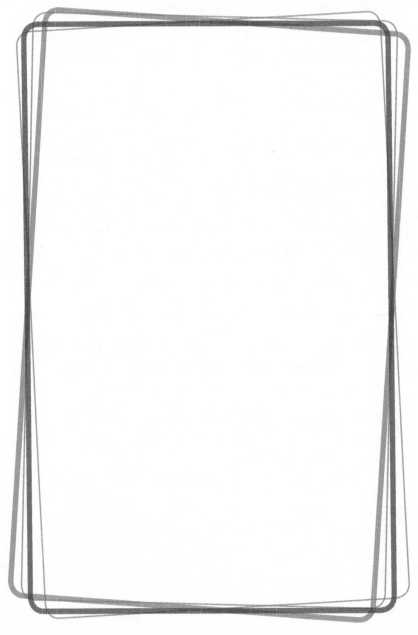

☐ Listening prayer (two-way journaling). This is a conversation between you and God. Start off by asking an open ended question in your journal below. Then wait to hear God's voice and write what you sense Him saying to you. See the appendix for sample questions.

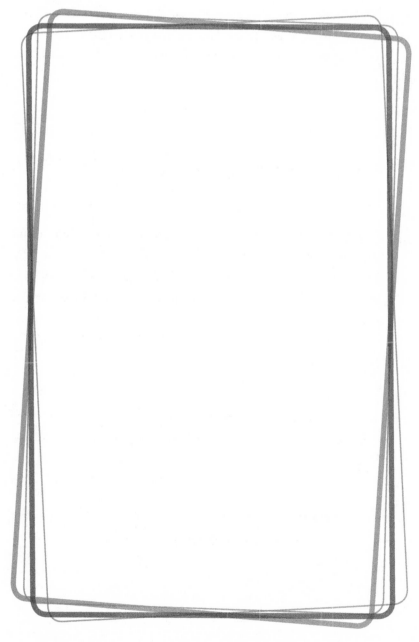

☐ Review the vision God has given you for your life, business, family, etc. Close your eyes, see it in your mind like a video and feel the emotions it brings. Write a summary here:

_____

☐ Write out or letter one godly affirmation below based on Scripture that you need to hear today. For example, I am loved.

☐ Pray for one of your weekly prayer requests. Write it here:

_____

☐ End your prayer time in gratitude, praise, and worship. Thank God for hearing your prayers and for anything else that comes to mind. Praise Him for what He has done for you and worship Him alone. As you worship, put your full focus on God and not on yourself.

Gratitude:

Praise:

Worship:

Date:_____

☐ Start with five minutes in silent meditation or with a breath prayer. See the appendix for examples.

☐ Begin with gratitude. Write out three things you are grateful for today. Be specific and include anything that happened in the last twenty-four hours.

Thank you, God, for:_____

Thank you, God, for:_____

Thank you, God, for:_____

☐ Take a moment to confess any sin from the last twenty-four hours and ask for God's forgiveness. _____

_____

_____

☐ Invite the Holy Spirit to teach you from the Scriptures today. *Holy Spirit come and open my mind so I can understand and receive what You have for me in Your Word. Reveal Yourself to me.*

☐ Bible reading. Write one takeaway from the verses you read today. If you prefer, choose a phrase that stuck out to you and write it out or letter it below.

Write out your prayers. Start off by writing everything that is currently on your heart and mind below. Pour out your heart to God (Psalms 62:8) and allow Him to clear your mind of the clutter. This will create space for you to hear God's still small voice (1 Kings 19:12) as you continue to journal on the next page.

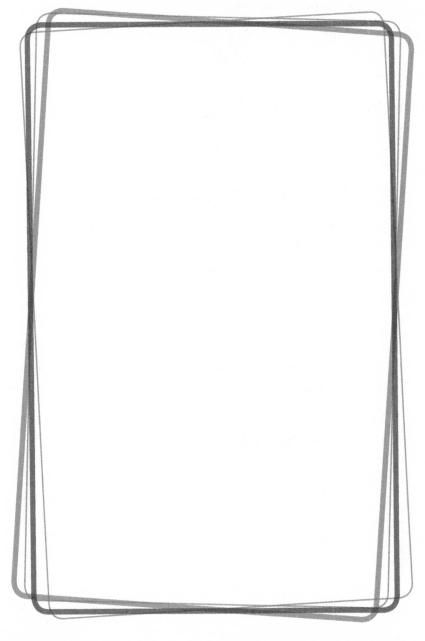

☐ Listening prayer (two-way journaling). This is a conversation between you and God. Start off by asking an open ended question in your journal below. Then wait to hear God's voice and write what you sense Him saying to you. See the appendix for sample questions.

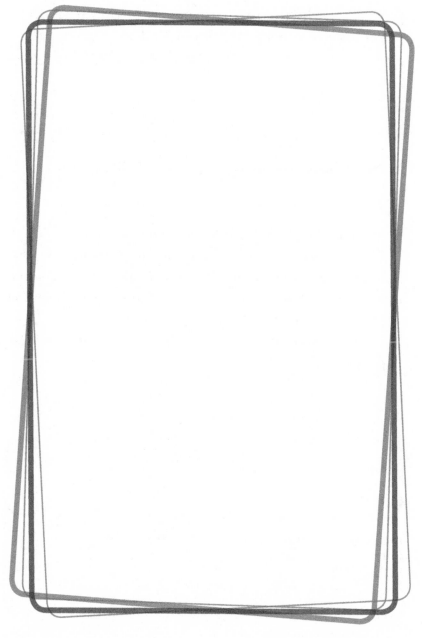

☐ Review the vision God has given you for your life, business, family, etc. Close your eyes, see it in your mind like a video and feel the emotions it brings. Write a summary here:

_____

☐ Write out or letter one godly affirmation below based on Scripture that you need to hear today. For example, I am loved.

☐ Pray for one of your weekly prayer requests. Write it here:

_____

☐ End your prayer time in gratitude, praise, and worship. Thank God for hearing your prayers and for anything else that comes to mind. Praise Him for what He has done for you and worship Him alone. As you worship, put your full focus on God and not on yourself.

Gratitude:

Praise:

Worship:

Date: _____

▱ Start with five minutes in silent meditation or with a breath prayer. See the appendix for examples.

▱ Begin with gratitude. Write out three things you are grateful for today. Be specific and include anything that happened in the last twenty-four hours.

Thank you, God, for: _____

Thank you, God, for: _____

Thank you, God, for: _____

▱ Take a moment to confess any sin from the last twenty-four hours and ask for God's forgiveness. _____

_____

_____

▱ Invite the Holy Spirit to teach you from the Scriptures today. *Holy Spirit come and open my mind so I can understand and receive what You have for me in Your Word. Reveal Yourself to me.*

▱ Bible reading. Write one takeaway from the verses you read today. If you prefer, choose a phrase that stuck out to you and write it out or letter it below.

Write out your prayers. Start off by writing everything that is currently on your heart and mind below. Pour out your heart to God (Psalms 62:8) and allow Him to clear your mind of the clutter. This will create space for you to hear God's still small voice (1 Kings 19:12) as you continue to journal on the next page.

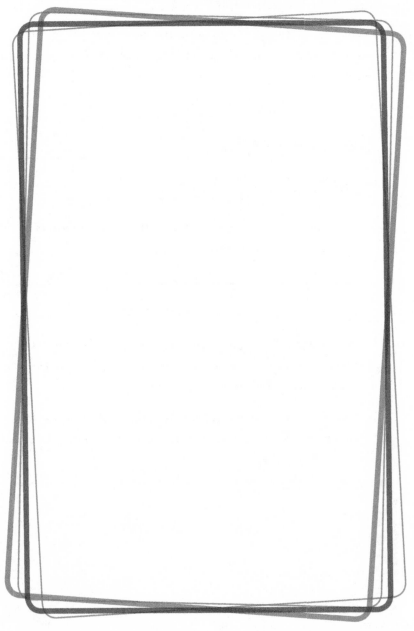

☐ Listening prayer (two-way journaling). This is a conversation between you and God. Start off by asking an open ended question in your journal below. Then wait to hear God's voice and write what you sense Him saying to you. See the appendix for sample questions.

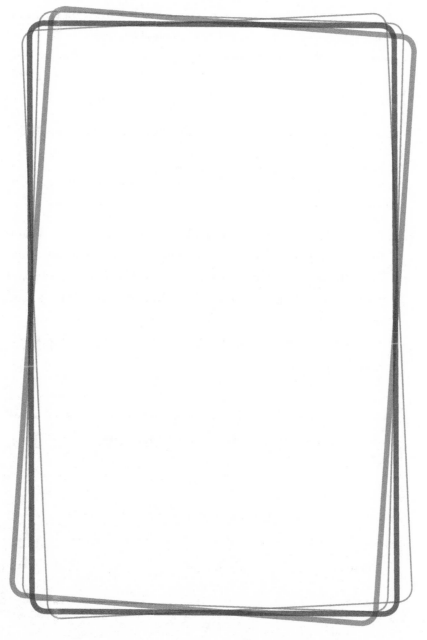

☐ Review the vision God has given you for your life, business, family, etc. Close your eyes, see it in your mind like a video and feel the emotions it brings. Write a summary here:

_____

☐ Write out or letter one godly affirmation below based on Scripture that you need to hear today. For example, I am loved.

☐ Pray for one of your weekly prayer requests. Write it here:

_____

☐ End your prayer time in gratitude, praise, and worship. Thank God for hearing your prayers and for anything else that comes to mind. Praise Him for what He has done for you and worship Him alone. As you worship, put your full focus on God and not on yourself.

Gratitude:

Praise:

Worship:

Date: _____

- ☐ Start with five minutes in silent meditation or with a breath prayer. See the appendix for examples.

- ☐ Begin with gratitude. Write out three things you are grateful for today. Be specific and include anything that happened in the last twenty-four hours.

*Thank you, God, for:*_____

*Thank you, God, for:*_____

*Thank you, God, for:*_____

- ☐ Take a moment to confess any sin from the last twenty-four hours and ask for God's forgiveness. _____

_____

_____

- ☐ Invite the Holy Spirit to teach you from the Scriptures today. *Holy Spirit come and open my mind so I can understand and receive what You have for me in Your Word. Reveal Yourself to me.*

- ☐ Bible reading. Write one takeaway from the verses you read today. If you prefer, choose a phrase that stuck out to you and write it out or letter it below.

Write out your prayers. Start off by writing everything that is currently on your heart and mind below. Pour out your heart to God (Psalms 62:8) and allow Him to clear your mind of the clutter. This will create space for you to hear God's still small voice (1 Kings 19:12) as you continue to journal on the next page.

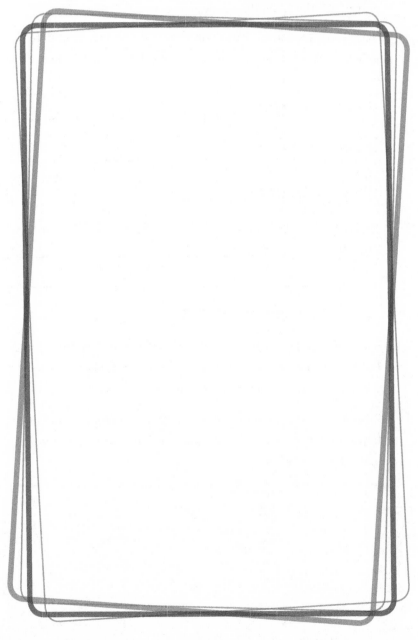

☐ Listening prayer (two-way journaling). This is a conversation between you and God. Start off by asking an open ended question in your journal below. Then wait to hear God's voice and write what you sense Him saying to you. See the appendix for sample questions.

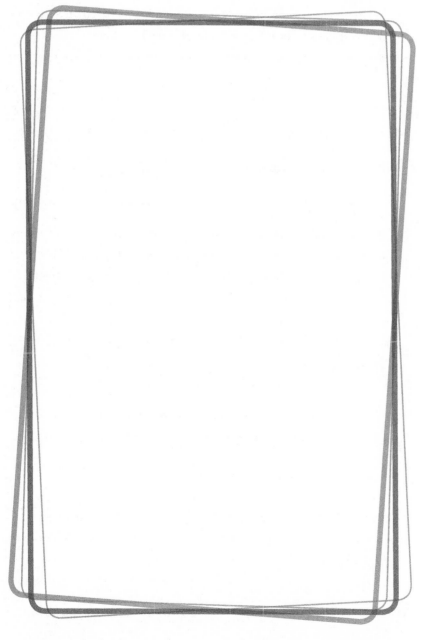

☐ Review the vision God has given you for your life, business, family, etc. Close your eyes, see it in your mind like a video and feel the emotions it brings. Write a summary here:

_____

☐ Write out or letter one godly affirmation below based on Scripture that you need to hear today. For example, I am loved.

┌─────────────────────────────────────┐
│   │
│   │
│   │
└─────────────────────────────────────┘

☐ Pray for one of your weekly prayer requests. Write it here:

_____

☐ End your prayer time in gratitude, praise, and worship. Thank God for hearing your prayers and for anything else that comes to mind. Praise Him for what He has done for you and worship Him alone. As you worship, put your full focus on God and not on yourself.

┌─────────────────────────────────────┐
│ *Gratitude*:   │
│   │
└─────────────────────────────────────┘

┌─────────────────────────────────────┐
│ *Praise*:   │
│   │
└─────────────────────────────────────┘

┌─────────────────────────────────────┐
│ *Worship*:   │
│   │
└─────────────────────────────────────┘

*Date:*_____

▱ Start with five minutes in silent meditation or with a breath prayer. See the appendix for examples.

▱ Begin with gratitude. Write out three things you are grateful for today. Be specific and include anything that happened in the last twenty-four hours.

*Thank you, God, for:*_____

*Thank you, God, for:*_____

*Thank you, God, for:*_____

▱ Take a moment to confess any sin from the last twenty-four hours and ask for God's forgiveness. _____

_____

_____

▱ Invite the Holy Spirit to teach you from the Scriptures today. *Holy Spirit come and open my mind so I can understand and receive what You have for me in Your Word. Reveal Yourself to me.*

▱ Bible reading. Write one takeaway from the verses you read today. If you prefer, choose a phrase that stuck out to you and write it out or letter it below.

Write out your prayers. Start off by writing everything that is currently on your heart and mind below. Pour out your heart to God (Psalms 62:8) and allow Him to clear your mind of the clutter. This will create space for you to hear God's still small voice (1 Kings 19:12) as you continue to journal on the next page.

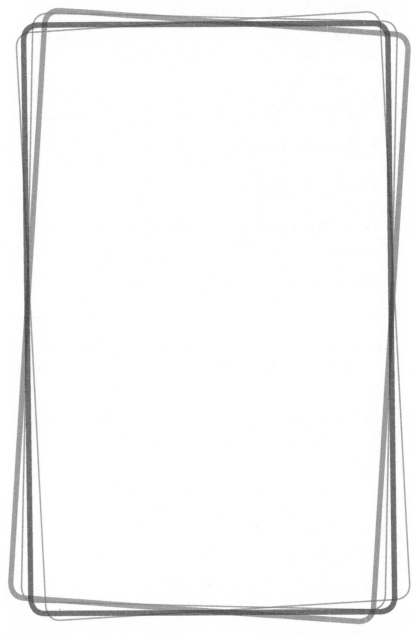

☐ Listening prayer (two-way journaling). This is a conversation between you and God. Start off by asking an open ended question in your journal below. Then wait to hear God's voice and write what you sense Him saying to you. See the appendix for sample questions.

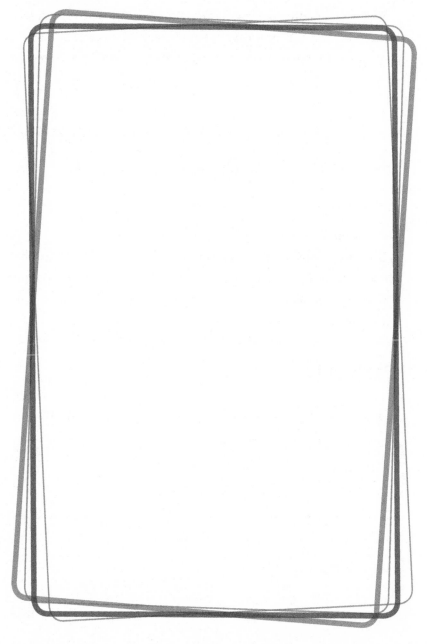

☐ Review the vision God has given you for your life, business, family, etc. Close your eyes, see it in your mind like a video and feel the emotions it brings. Write a summary here:

_____

☐ Write out or letter one godly affirmation below based on Scripture that you need to hear today. For example, I am loved.

☐ Pray for one of your weekly prayer requests. Write it here:

_____

☐ End your prayer time in gratitude, praise, and worship. Thank God for hearing your prayers and for anything else that comes to mind. Praise Him for what He has done for you and worship Him alone. As you worship, put your full focus on God and not on yourself.

Gratitude:

Praise:

Worship:

Date: _____

- [ ] Start with five minutes in silent meditation or with a breath prayer. See the appendix for examples.

- [ ] Begin with gratitude. Write out three things you are grateful for today. Be specific and include anything that happened in the last twenty-four hours.

Thank you, God, for: _____

Thank you, God, for: _____

Thank you, God, for: _____

- [ ] Take a moment to confess any sin from the last twenty-four hours and ask for God's forgiveness. _____

_____

_____

- [ ] Invite the Holy Spirit to teach you from the Scriptures today. *Holy Spirit come and open my mind so I can understand and receive what You have for me in Your Word. Reveal Yourself to me.*

- [ ] Bible reading. Write one takeaway from the verses you read today. If you prefer, choose a phrase that stuck out to you and write it out or letter it below.

Write out your prayers. Start off by writing everything that is currently on your heart and mind below. Pour out your heart to God (Psalms 62:8) and allow Him to clear your mind of the clutter. This will create space for you to hear God's still small voice (1 Kings 19:12) as you continue to journal on the next page.

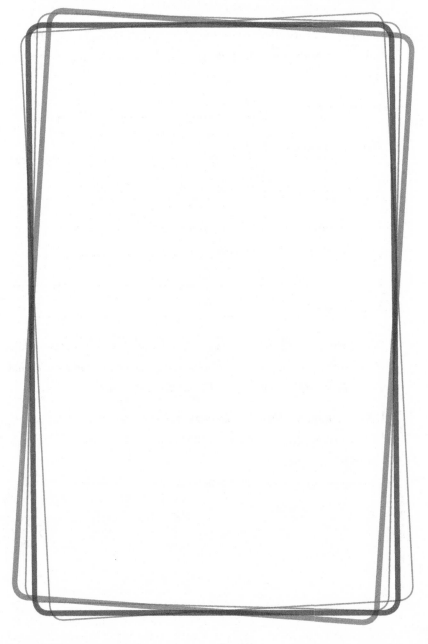

Listening prayer (two-way journaling). This is a conversation between you and God. Start off by asking an open ended question in your journal below. Then wait to hear God's voice and write what you sense Him saying to you. See the appendix for sample questions.

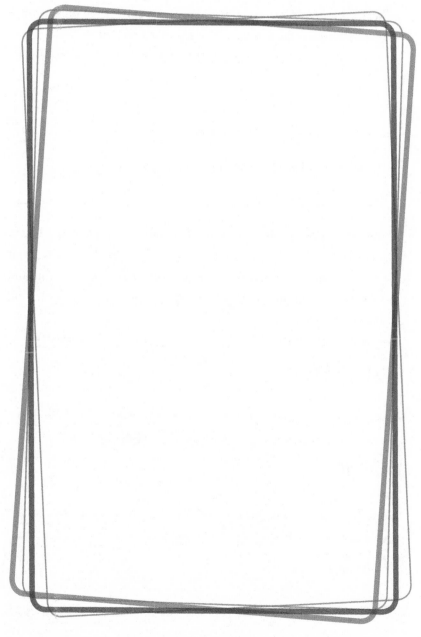

☐ Review the vision God has given you for your life, business, family, etc. Close your eyes, see it in your mind like a video and feel the emotions it brings. Write a summary here:

_____

☐ Write out or letter one godly affirmation below based on Scripture that you need to hear today. For example, I am loved.

☐ Pray for one of your weekly prayer requests. Write it here:

_____

☐ End your prayer time in gratitude, praise, and worship. Thank God for hearing your prayers and for anything else that comes to mind. Praise Him for what He has done for you and worship Him alone. As you worship, put your full focus on God and not on yourself.

Gratitude:

Praise:

Worship:

Date: _____

☐ Start with five minutes in silent meditation or with a breath prayer. See the appendix for examples.

☐ Begin with gratitude. Write out three things you are grateful for today. Be specific and include anything that happened in the last twenty-four hours.

Thank you, God, for: _____

Thank you, God, for: _____

Thank you, God, for: _____

☐ Take a moment to confess any sin from the last twenty-four hours and ask for God's forgiveness. _____

_____

_____

☐ Invite the Holy Spirit to teach you from the Scriptures today. *Holy Spirit come and open my mind so I can understand and receive what You have for me in Your Word. Reveal Yourself to me.*

☐ Bible reading. Write one takeaway from the verses you read today. If you prefer, choose a phrase that stuck out to you and write it out or letter it below.

Write out your prayers. Start off by writing everything that is currently on your heart and mind below. Pour out your heart to God (Psalms 62:8) and allow Him to clear your mind of the clutter. This will create space for you to hear God's still small voice (1 Kings 19:12) as you continue to journal on the next page.

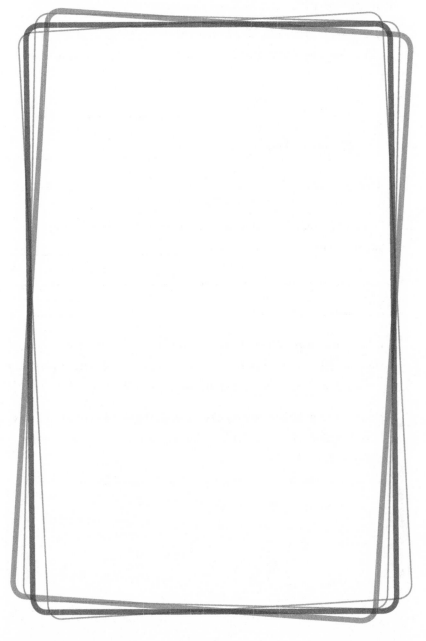

☐ Listening prayer (two-way journaling). This is a conversation between you and God. Start off by asking an open ended question in your journal below. Then wait to hear God's voice and write what you sense Him saying to you. See the appendix for sample questions.

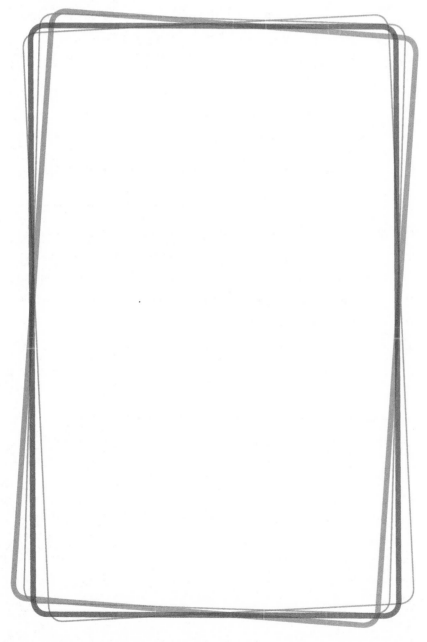

☐ Review the vision God has given you for your life, business, family, etc. Close your eyes, see it in your mind like a video and feel the emotions it brings. Write a summary here:

_____

☐ Write out or letter one godly affirmation below based on Scripture that you need to hear today. For example, I am loved.

_____

☐ Pray for one of your weekly prayer requests. Write it here:

_____

☐ End your prayer time in gratitude, praise, and worship. Thank God for hearing your prayers and for anything else that comes to mind. Praise Him for what He has done for you and worship Him alone. As you worship, put your full focus on God and not on yourself.

Gratitude:

Praise:

Worship:

The earnest prayer OF A person RIGHTEOUS HAS great power & PRODUCES wonderful RESULTS

JAMES 5:16B

Weekly Prayer Requests

Date: _____

family: Date answered: _____

_____

_____

_____

friends: Date answered: _____

_____

_____

_____

the world: Date answered: _____

_____

_____

_____

myself: Date answered: _____

_____

_____

_____

other: Date answered: _____

_____

_____

_____

☐ Once a week, spend time asking God for His vision for your life, business, etc. Proverbs 29:18 says, "Without vision, we perish" (KJV).

1. God, show me your vision for: _____
   (my life, my business, my marriage).
2. Ask God for a picture. See yourself in the vision God has for you. Close your eyes and visualize. Write out or sketch what you see below.
3. What will it feel like? Ask God for an emotion to attach to the vision He has for you. This is powerful! Write about it below.

God, show me your vision for:

Thank God for what He showed you below. Then ask Him, "Lord, is there more?

Close your eyes and look for more in the picture God gave you. Write out or sketch what you see below.

Lord, is there more?

Date: _____

⟋⟋⟋⟋⟋⟋⟋⟋⟋⟋

☐ Start with five minutes in silent meditation or with a breath prayer. See the appendix for examples.

☐ Begin with gratitude. Write out three things you are grateful for today. Be specific and include anything that happened in the last twenty-four hours.

*Thank you, God, for:*_____

*Thank you, God, for:*_____

*Thank you, God, for:*_____

☐ Take a moment to confess any sin from the last twenty-four hours and ask for God's forgiveness. _____

_____

_____

☐ Invite the Holy Spirit to teach you from the Scriptures today. *Holy Spirit come and open my mind so I can understand and receive what You have for me in Your Word. Reveal Yourself to me.*

☐ Bible reading. Write one takeaway from the verses you read today. If you prefer, choose a phrase that stuck out to you and write it out or letter it below.

☐ Write out your prayers. Start off by writing everything that is currently on your heart and mind below. Pour out your heart to God (Psalms 62:8) and allow Him to clear your mind of the clutter. This will create space for you to hear God's still small voice (1 Kings 19:12) as you continue to journal on the next page.

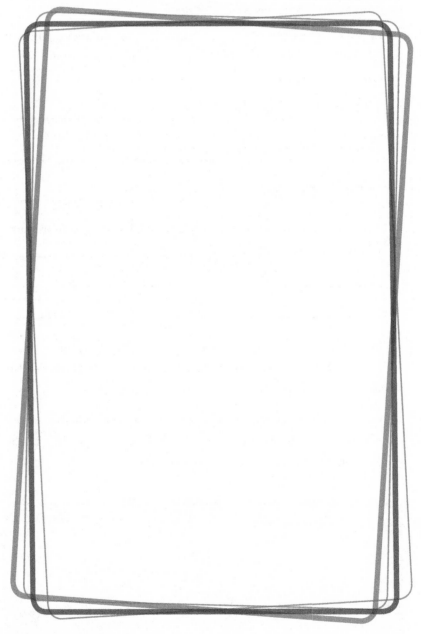

☐ Listening prayer (two-way journaling). This is a conversation between you and God. Start off by asking an open ended question in your journal below. Then wait to hear God's voice and write what you sense Him saying to you. See the appendix for sample questions.

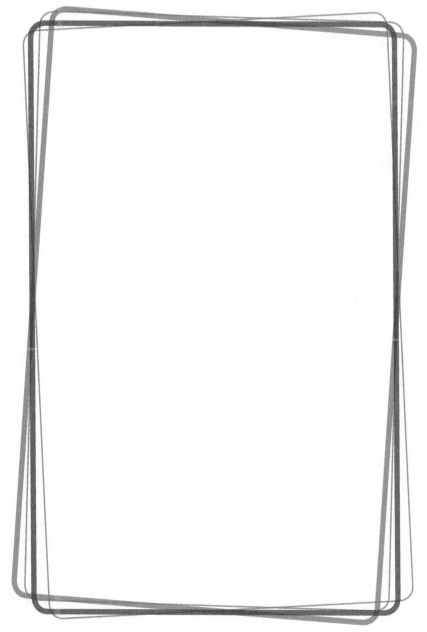

☐ Review the vision God has given you for your life, business, family, etc. Close your eyes, see it in your mind like a video and feel the emotions it brings. Write a summary here:

_____

☐ Write out or letter one godly affirmation below based on Scripture that you need to hear today. For example, I am loved.

☐ Pray for one of your weekly prayer requests. Write it here:

_____

☐ End your prayer time in gratitude, praise, and worship. Thank God for hearing your prayers and for anything else that comes to mind. Praise Him for what He has done for you and worship Him alone. As you worship, put your full focus on God and not on yourself.

Gratitude:

Praise:

Worship:

Date: _____

☐ Start with five minutes in silent meditation or with a breath prayer. See the appendix for examples.

☐ Begin with gratitude. Write out three things you are grateful for today. Be specific and include anything that happened in the last twenty-four hours.

Thank you, God, for: _____

Thank you, God, for: _____

Thank you, God, for: _____

☐ Take a moment to confess any sin from the last twenty-four hours and ask for God's forgiveness. _____

_____

_____

☐ Invite the Holy Spirit to teach you from the Scriptures today. *Holy Spirit come and open my mind so I can understand and receive what You have for me in Your Word. Reveal Yourself to me.*

☐ Bible reading. Write one takeaway from the verses you read today. If you prefer, choose a phrase that stuck out to you and write it out or letter it below.

Write out your prayers. Start off by writing everything that is currently on your heart and mind below. Pour out your heart to God (Psalms 62:8) and allow Him to clear your mind of the clutter. This will create space for you to hear God's still small voice (1 Kings 19:12) as you continue to journal on the next page.

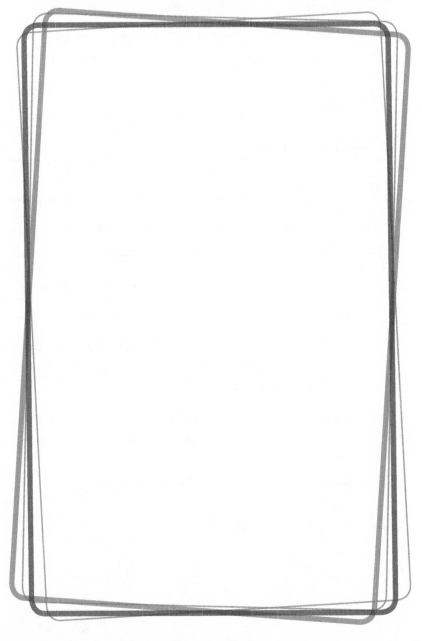

☐ Listening prayer (two-way journaling). This is a conversation between you and God. Start off by asking an open ended question in your journal below. Then wait to hear God's voice and write what you sense Him saying to you. See the appendix for sample questions.

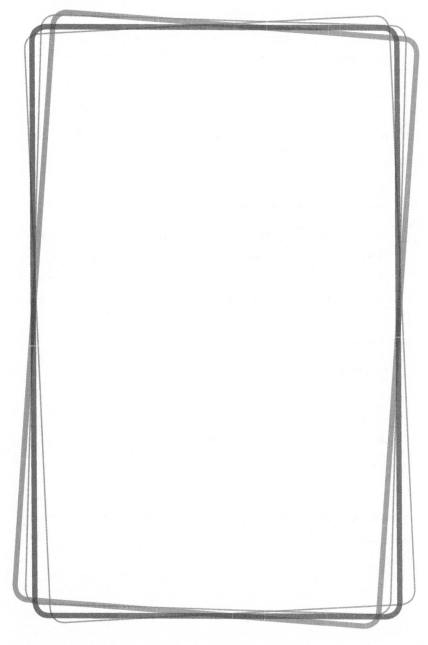

☐ Review the vision God has given you for your life, business, family, etc. Close your eyes, see it in your mind like a video and feel the emotions it brings. Write a summary here:

_____

☐ Write out or letter one godly affirmation below based on Scripture that you need to hear today. For example, I am loved.

☐ Pray for one of your weekly prayer requests. Write it here:

_____

☐ End your prayer time in gratitude, praise, and worship. Thank God for hearing your prayers and for anything else that comes to mind. Praise Him for what He has done for you and worship Him alone. As you worship, put your full focus on God and not on yourself.

Gratitude:

Praise:

Worship:

Date: _____

☐ Start with five minutes in silent meditation or with a breath prayer. See the appendix for examples.

☐ Begin with gratitude. Write out three things you are grateful for today. Be specific and include anything that happened in the last twenty-four hours.

Thank you, God, for: _____

Thank you, God, for: _____

Thank you, God, for: _____

☐ Take a moment to confess any sin from the last twenty-four hours and ask for God's forgiveness. _____

_____

_____

☐ Invite the Holy Spirit to teach you from the Scriptures today. *Holy Spirit come and open my mind so I can understand and receive what You have for me in Your Word. Reveal Yourself to me.*

☐ Bible reading. Write one takeaway from the verses you read today. If you prefer, choose a phrase that stuck out to you and write it out or letter it below.

Write out your prayers. Start off by writing everything that is currently on your heart and mind below. Pour out your heart to God (Psalms 62:8) and allow Him to clear your mind of the clutter. This will create space for you to hear God's still small voice (1 Kings 19:12) as you continue to journal on the next page.

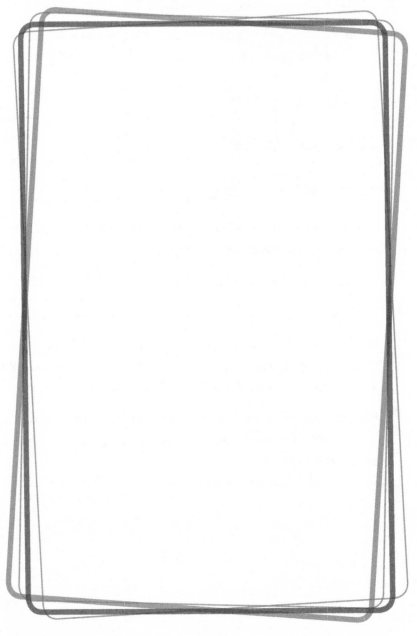

☐ Listening prayer (two-way journaling). This is a conversation between you and God. Start off by asking an open ended question in your journal below. Then wait to hear God's voice and write what you sense Him saying to you. See the appendix for sample questions.

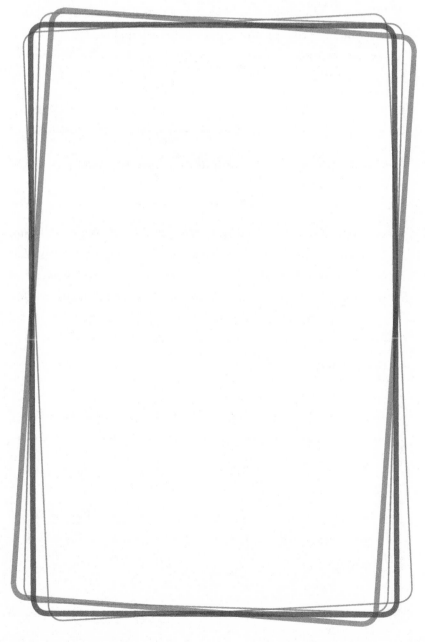

☐ Review the vision God has given you for your life, business, family, etc. Close your eyes, see it in your mind like a video and feel the emotions it brings. Write a summary here:

_____

☐ Write out or letter one godly affirmation below based on Scripture that you need to hear today. For example, I am loved.

☐ Pray for one of your weekly prayer requests. Write it here:

_____

☐ End your prayer time in gratitude, praise, and worship. Thank God for hearing your prayers and for anything else that comes to mind. Praise Him for what He has done for you and worship Him alone. As you worship, put your full focus on God and not on yourself.

Gratitude:

Praise:

Worship:

Date: _____

☐ Start with five minutes in silent meditation or with a breath prayer. See the appendix for examples.

☐ Begin with gratitude. Write out three things you are grateful for today. Be specific and include anything that happened in the last twenty-four hours.

Thank you, God, for: _____

Thank you, God, for: _____

Thank you, God, for: _____

☐ Take a moment to confess any sin from the last twenty-four hours and ask for God's forgiveness. _____

_____

_____

☐ Invite the Holy Spirit to teach you from the Scriptures today. *Holy Spirit come and open my mind so I can understand and receive what You have for me in Your Word. Reveal Yourself to me.*

☐ Bible reading. Write one takeaway from the verses you read today. If you prefer, choose a phrase that stuck out to you and write it out or letter it below.

Write out your prayers. Start off by writing everything that is currently on your heart and mind below. Pour out your heart to God (Psalms 62:8) and allow Him to clear your mind of the clutter. This will create space for you to hear God's still small voice (1 Kings 19:12) as you continue to journal on the next page.

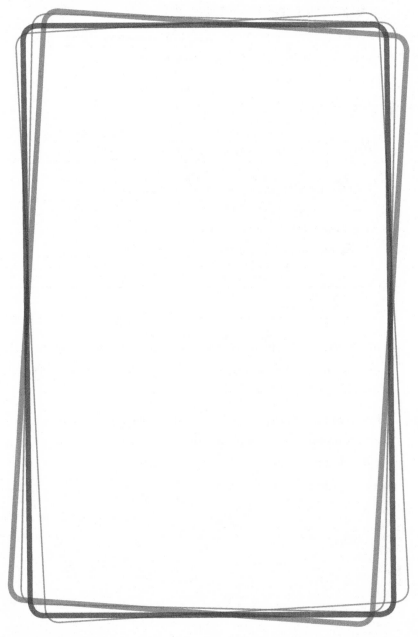

☐ Listening prayer (two-way journaling). This is a conversation between you and God. Start off by asking an open ended question in your journal below. Then wait to hear God's voice and write what you sense Him saying to you. See the appendix for sample questions.

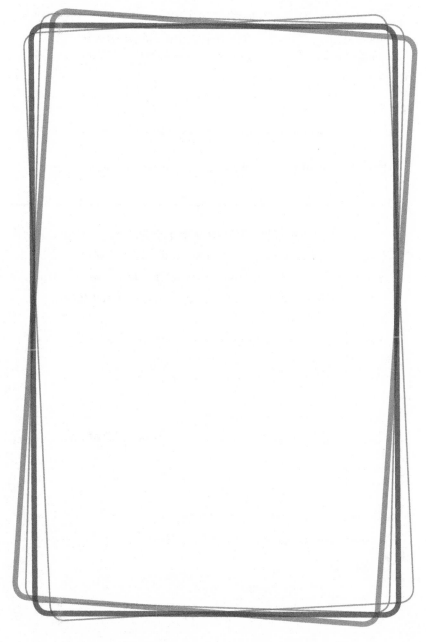

☐ Review the vision God has given you for your life, business, family, etc. Close your eyes, see it in your mind like a video and feel the emotions it brings. Write a summary here:

_____

☐ Write out or letter one godly affirmation below based on Scripture that you need to hear today. For example, I am loved.

_____

☐ Pray for one of your weekly prayer requests. Write it here:

_____

☐ End your prayer time in gratitude, praise, and worship. Thank God for hearing your prayers and for anything else that comes to mind. Praise Him for what He has done for you and worship Him alone. As you worship, put your full focus on God and not on yourself.

Gratitude:

Praise:

Worship:

Date: _____

☐ Start with five minutes in silent meditation or with a breath prayer. See the appendix for examples.

☐ Begin with gratitude. Write out three things you are grateful for today. Be specific and include anything that happened in the last twenty-four hours.

Thank you, God, for: _____

Thank you, God, for: _____

Thank you, God, for: _____

☐ Take a moment to confess any sin from the last twenty-four hours and ask for God's forgiveness. _____

_____

_____

☐ Invite the Holy Spirit to teach you from the Scriptures today. *Holy Spirit come and open my mind so I can understand and receive what You have for me in Your Word. Reveal Yourself to me.*

☐ Bible reading. Write one takeaway from the verses you read today. If you prefer, choose a phrase that stuck out to you and write it out or letter it below.

Write out your prayers. Start off by writing everything that is currently on your heart and mind below. Pour out your heart to God (Psalms 62:8) and allow Him to clear your mind of the clutter. This will create space for you to hear God's still small voice (1 Kings 19:12) as you continue to journal on the next page.

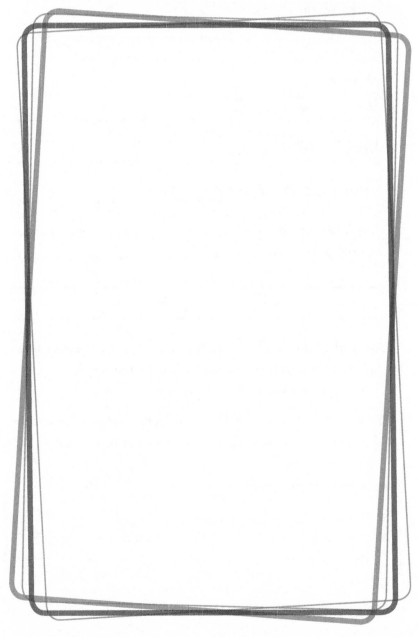

☐ Listening prayer (two-way journaling). This is a conversation between you and God. Start off by asking an open ended question in your journal below. Then wait to hear God's voice and write what you sense Him saying to you. See the appendix for sample questions.

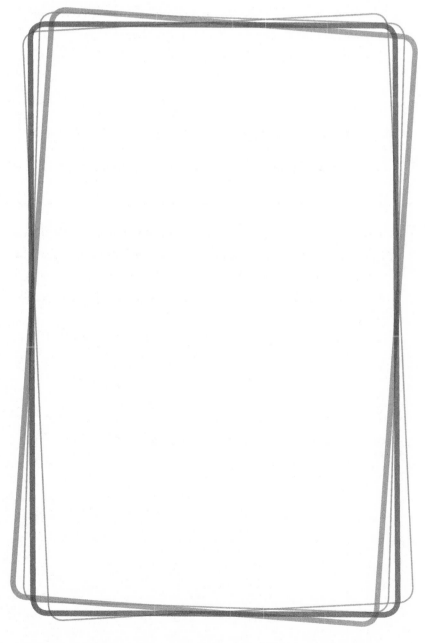

☐ Review the vision God has given you for your life, business, family, etc. Close your eyes, see it in your mind like a video and feel the emotions it brings. Write a summary here:

_____

☐ Write out or letter one godly affirmation below based on Scripture that you need to hear today. For example, I am loved.

☐ Pray for one of your weekly prayer requests. Write it here:

_____

☐ End your prayer time in gratitude, praise, and worship. Thank God for hearing your prayers and for anything else that comes to mind. Praise Him for what He has done for you and worship Him alone. As you worship, put your full focus on God and not on yourself.

Gratitude:

Praise:

Worship:

Date: _____

Start with five minutes in silent meditation or with a breath prayer. See the appendix for examples.

Begin with gratitude. Write out three things you are grateful for today. Be specific and include anything that happened in the last twenty-four hours.

Thank you, God, for: _____

Thank you, God, for: _____

Thank you, God, for: _____

Take a moment to confess any sin from the last twenty-four hours and ask for God's forgiveness. _____

_____

_____

Invite the Holy Spirit to teach you from the Scriptures today. *Holy Spirit come and open my mind so I can understand and receive what You have for me in Your Word. Reveal Yourself to me.*

Bible reading. Write one takeaway from the verses you read today. If you prefer, choose a phrase that stuck out to you and write it out or letter it below.

Write out your prayers. Start off by writing everything that is currently on your heart and mind below. Pour out your heart to God (Psalms 62:8) and allow Him to clear your mind of the clutter. This will create space for you to hear God's still small voice (1 Kings 19:12) as you continue to journal on the next page.

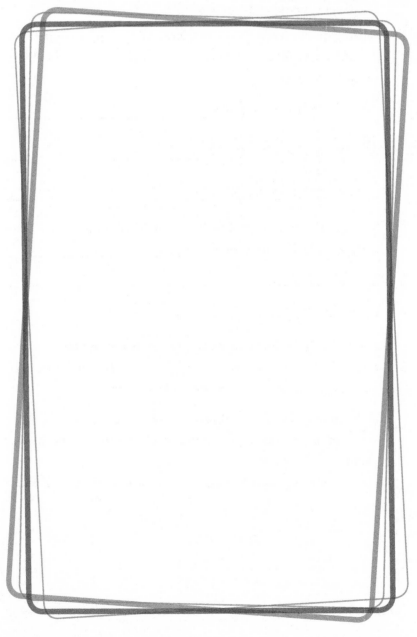

Listening prayer (two-way journaling). This is a conversation between you and God. Start off by asking an open ended question in your journal below. Then wait to hear God's voice and write what you sense Him saying to you. See the appendix for sample questions.

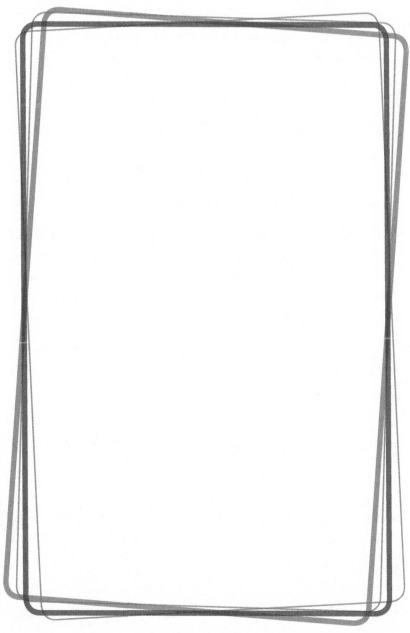

☐ Review the vision God has given you for your life, business, family, etc. Close your eyes, see it in your mind like a video and feel the emotions it brings. Write a summary here:

_____

☐ Write out or letter one godly affirmation below based on Scripture that you need to hear today. For example, I am loved.

☐ Pray for one of your weekly prayer requests. Write it here:

_____

☐ End your prayer time in gratitude, praise, and worship. Thank God for hearing your prayers and for anything else that comes to mind. Praise Him for what He has done for you and worship Him alone. As you worship, put your full focus on God and not on yourself.

Gratitude:

Praise:

Worship:

Date: _____

☐ Start with five minutes in silent meditation or with a breath prayer. See the appendix for examples.

☐ Begin with gratitude. Write out three things you are grateful for today. Be specific and include anything that happened in the last twenty-four hours.

Thank you, God, for: _____

Thank you, God, for: _____

Thank you, God, for: _____

☐ Take a moment to confess any sin from the last twenty-four hours and ask for God's forgiveness. _____

_____

_____

☐ Invite the Holy Spirit to teach you from the Scriptures today. *Holy Spirit come and open my mind so I can understand and receive what You have for me in Your Word. Reveal Yourself to me.*

☐ Bible reading. Write one takeaway from the verses you read today. If you prefer, choose a phrase that stuck out to you and write it out or letter it below.

Write out your prayers. Start off by writing everything that is currently on your heart and mind below. Pour out your heart to God (Psalms 62:8) and allow Him to clear your mind of the clutter. This will create space for you to hear God's still small voice (1 Kings 19:12) as you continue to journal on the next page.

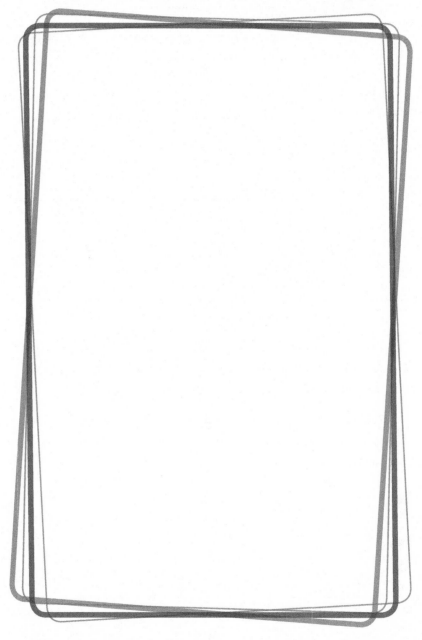

☐ Listening prayer (two-way journaling). This is a conversation between you and God. Start off by asking an open ended question in your journal below. Then wait to hear God's voice and write what you sense Him saying to you. See the appendix for sample questions.

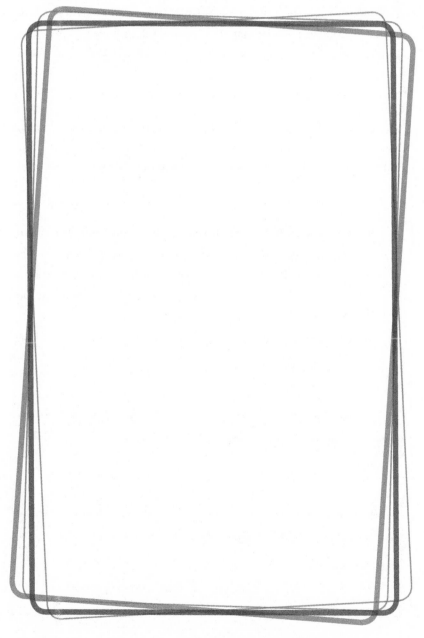

☐ Review the vision God has given you for your life, business, family, etc. Close your eyes, see it in your mind like a video and feel the emotions it brings. Write a summary here:

_____

☐ Write out or letter one godly affirmation below based on Scripture that you need to hear today. For example, I am loved.

☐ Pray for one of your weekly prayer requests. Write it here:

_____

☐ End your prayer time in gratitude, praise, and worship. Thank God for hearing your prayers and for anything else that comes to mind. Praise Him for what He has done for you and worship Him alone. As you worship, put your full focus on God and not on yourself.

Gratitude:

Praise:

Worship:

Prayer DOES NOT CHANGE *God* BUT IT CHANGES *him who prays*

SOREN KIERKEGAARD

Weekly Prayer Requests

Date:_____

family: Date answered: _____

_____

_____

_____

friends: Date answered: _____

_____

_____

_____

the world: Date answered: _____

_____

_____

_____

myself: Date answered: _____

_____

_____

_____

other: Date answered: _____

_____

_____

_____

☐ Once a week, spend time asking God for His vision for your life, business, etc. Proverbs 29:18 says, "Without vision, we perish" (KJV).

1. God, show me your vision for: _____ (my life, my business, my marriage).
2. Ask God for a picture. See yourself in the vision God has for you. Close your eyes and visualize. Write out or sketch what you see below.
3. What will it feel like? Ask God for an emotion to attach to the vision He has for you. This is powerful! Write about it below.

God, show me your vision for:

☐ Thank God for what He showed you below. Then ask Him, "Lord, is there more?

Close your eyes and look for more in the picture God gave you. Write out or sketch what you see below.

Lord, is there more?

Date: _____

☐ Start with five minutes in silent meditation or with a breath prayer. See the appendix for examples.

☐ Begin with gratitude. Write out three things you are grateful for today. Be specific and include anything that happened in the last twenty-four hours.

Thank you, God, for: _____

Thank you, God, for: _____

Thank you, God, for: _____

☐ Take a moment to confess any sin from the last twenty-four hours and ask for God's forgiveness. _____

_____

_____

☐ Invite the Holy Spirit to teach you from the Scriptures today. *Holy Spirit come and open my mind so I can understand and receive what You have for me in Your Word. Reveal Yourself to me.*

☐ Bible reading. Write one takeaway from the verses you read today. If you prefer, choose a phrase that stuck out to you and write it out or letter it below.

Write out your prayers. Start off by writing everything that is currently on your heart and mind below. Pour out your heart to God (Psalms 62:8) and allow Him to clear your mind of the clutter. This will create space for you to hear God's still small voice (1 Kings 19:12) as you continue to journal on the next page.

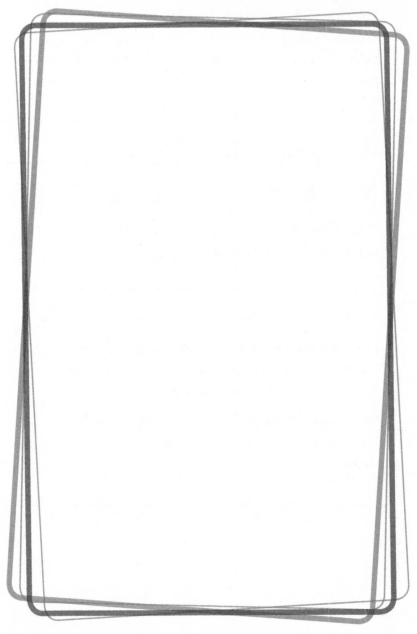

☐ Listening prayer (two-way journaling). This is a conversation between you and God. Start off by asking an open ended question in your journal below. Then wait to hear God's voice and write what you sense Him saying to you. See the appendix for sample questions.

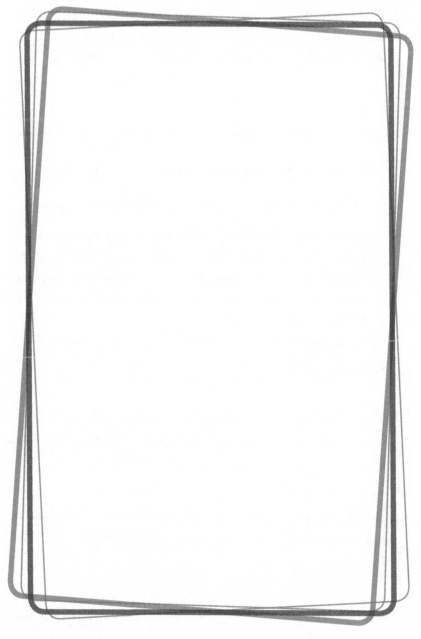

☐ Review the vision God has given you for your life, business, family, etc. Close your eyes, see it in your mind like a video and feel the emotions it brings. Write a summary here:

_____

☐ Write out or letter one godly affirmation below based on Scripture that you need to hear today. For example, I am loved.

_____

☐ Pray for one of your weekly prayer requests. Write it here:

_____

☐ End your prayer time in gratitude, praise, and worship. Thank God for hearing your prayers and for anything else that comes to mind. Praise Him for what He has done for you and worship Him alone. As you worship, put your full focus on God and not on yourself.

Gratitude:

Praise:

Worship:

Date: _____

☐ Start with five minutes in silent meditation or with a breath prayer. See the appendix for examples.

☐ Begin with gratitude. Write out three things you are grateful for today. Be specific and include anything that happened in the last twenty-four hours.

Thank you, God, for: _____

Thank you, God, for: _____

Thank you, God, for: _____

☐ Take a moment to confess any sin from the last twenty-four hours and ask for God's forgiveness. _____

_____

_____

☐ Invite the Holy Spirit to teach you from the Scriptures today. *Holy Spirit come and open my mind so I can understand and receive what You have for me in Your Word. Reveal Yourself to me.*

☐ Bible reading. Write one takeaway from the verses you read today. If you prefer, choose a phrase that stuck out to you and write it out or letter it below.

Write out your prayers. Start off by writing everything that is currently on your heart and mind below. Pour out your heart to God (Psalms 62:8) and allow Him to clear your mind of the clutter. This will create space for you to hear God's still small voice (1 Kings 19:12) as you continue to journal on the next page.

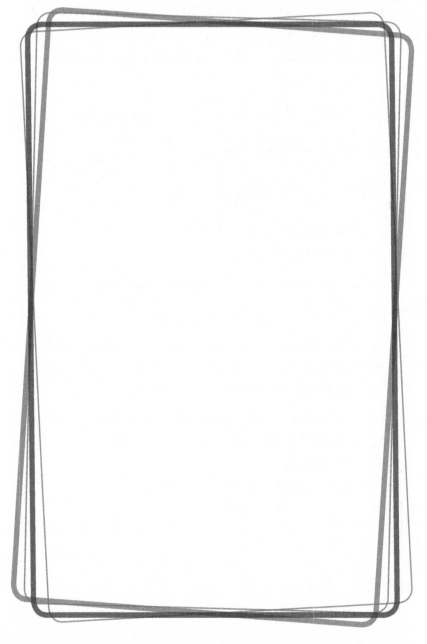

Listening prayer (two-way journaling). This is a conversation between you and God. Start off by asking an open ended question in your journal below. Then wait to hear God's voice and write what you sense Him saying to you. See the appendix for sample questions.

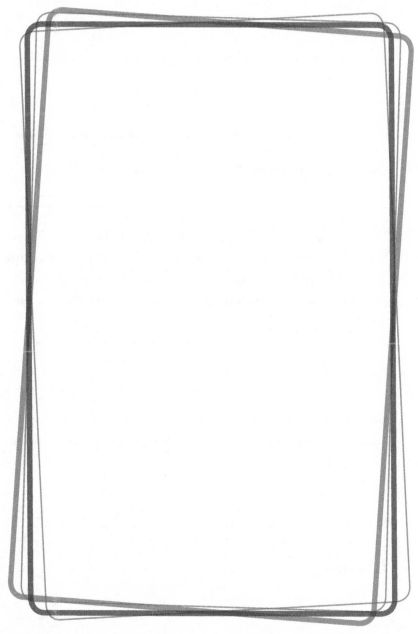

☐ Review the vision God has given you for your life, business, family, etc. Close your eyes, see it in your mind like a video and feel the emotions it brings. Write a summary here:

_____

☐ Write out or letter one godly affirmation below based on Scripture that you need to hear today. For example, I am loved.

☐ Pray for one of your weekly prayer requests. Write it here:

_____

☐ End your prayer time in gratitude, praise, and worship. Thank God for hearing your prayers and for anything else that comes to mind. Praise Him for what He has done for you and worship Him alone. As you worship, put your full focus on God and not on yourself.

Gratitude:

Praise:

Worship:

Date: _____

☐ Start with five minutes in silent meditation or with a breath prayer. See the appendix for examples.

☐ Begin with gratitude. Write out three things you are grateful for today. Be specific and include anything that happened in the last twenty-four hours.

Thank you, God, for: _____

Thank you, God, for: _____

Thank you, God, for: _____

☐ Take a moment to confess any sin from the last twenty-four hours and ask for God's forgiveness. _____

_____

_____

☐ Invite the Holy Spirit to teach you from the Scriptures today. *Holy Spirit come and open my mind so I can understand and receive what You have for me in Your Word. Reveal Yourself to me.*

☐ Bible reading. Write one takeaway from the verses you read today. If you prefer, choose a phrase that stuck out to you and write it out or letter it below.

Write out your prayers. Start off by writing everything that is currently on your heart and mind below. Pour out your heart to God (Psalms 62:8) and allow Him to clear your mind of the clutter. This will create space for you to hear God's still small voice (1 Kings 19:12) as you continue to journal on the next page.

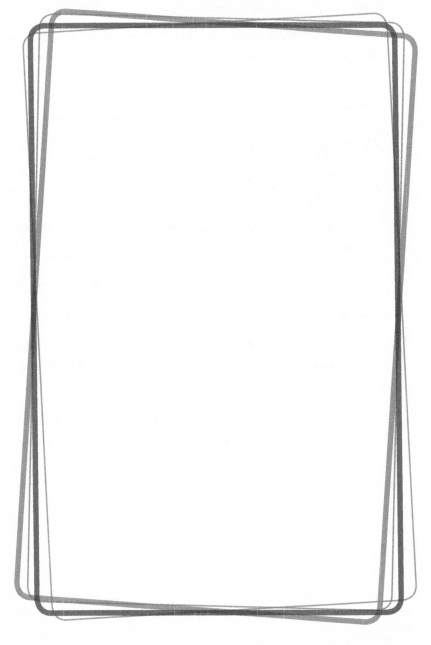

☐ Listening prayer (two-way journaling). This is a conversation between you and God. Start off by asking an open ended question in your journal below. Then wait to hear God's voice and write what you sense Him saying to you. See the appendix for sample questions.

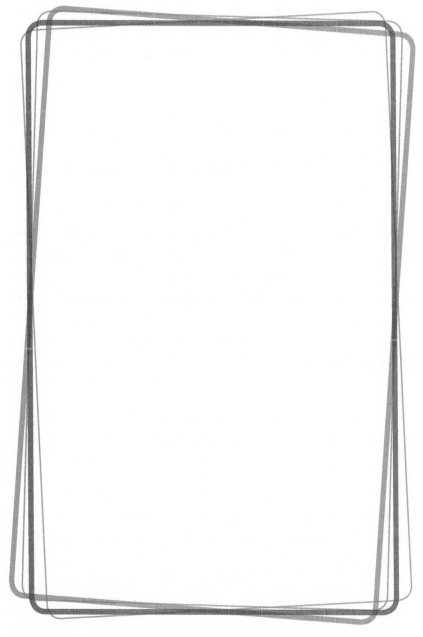

☐ Review the vision God has given you for your life, business, family, etc. Close your eyes, see it in your mind like a video and feel the emotions it brings. Write a summary here:

_____

☐ Write out or letter one godly affirmation below based on Scripture that you need to hear today. For example, I am loved.

```
┌─────────────────────────────────────────────┐
│                                             │
│                                             │
│                                             │
└─────────────────────────────────────────────┘
```

☐ Pray for one of your weekly prayer requests. Write it here:

_____

☐ End your prayer time in gratitude, praise, and worship. Thank God for hearing your prayers and for anything else that comes to mind. Praise Him for what He has done for you and worship Him alone. As you worship, put your full focus on God and not on yourself.

```
┌─────────────────────────────────────────────┐
│ Gratitude:                                  │
│                                             │
└─────────────────────────────────────────────┘
```

```
┌─────────────────────────────────────────────┐
│ Praise:                                     │
│                                             │
└─────────────────────────────────────────────┘
```

```
┌─────────────────────────────────────────────┐
│ Worship:                                    │
│                                             │
└─────────────────────────────────────────────┘
```

Date: _____

☐ Start with five minutes in silent meditation or with a breath prayer. See the appendix for examples.

☐ Begin with gratitude. Write out three things you are grateful for today. Be specific and include anything that happened in the last twenty-four hours.

Thank you, God, for: _____

Thank you, God, for: _____

Thank you, God, for: _____

☐ Take a moment to confess any sin from the last twenty-four hours and ask for God's forgiveness. _____

_____

_____

☐ Invite the Holy Spirit to teach you from the Scriptures today. *Holy Spirit come and open my mind so I can understand and receive what You have for me in Your Word. Reveal Yourself to me.*

☐ Bible reading. Write one takeaway from the verses you read today. If you prefer, choose a phrase that stuck out to you and write it out or letter it below.

Write out your prayers. Start off by writing everything that is currently on your heart and mind below. Pour out your heart to God (Psalms 62:8) and allow Him to clear your mind of the clutter. This will create space for you to hear God's still small voice (1 Kings 19:12) as you continue to journal on the next page.

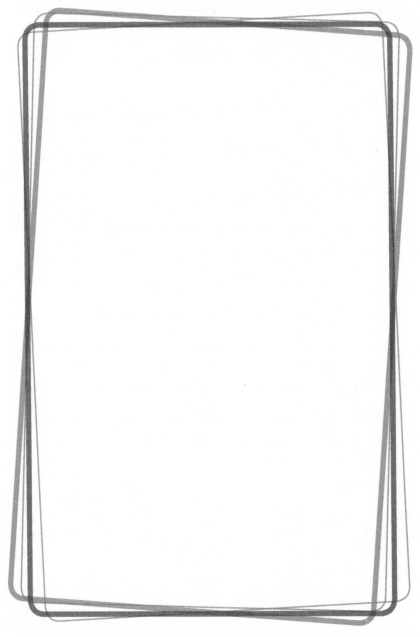

Listening prayer (two-way journaling). This is a conversation between you and God. Start off by asking an open ended question in your journal below. Then wait to hear God's voice and write what you sense Him saying to you. See the appendix for sample questions.

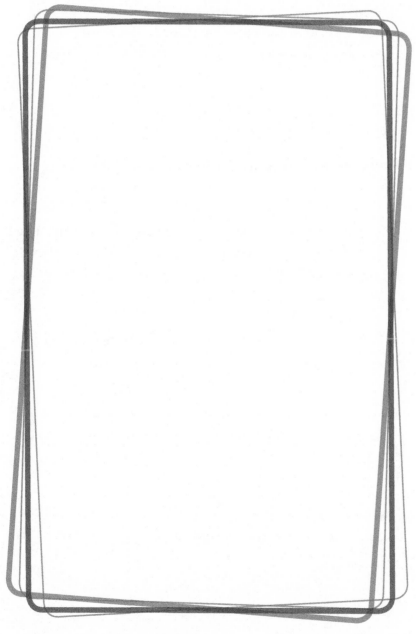

☐ Review the vision God has given you for your life, business, family, etc. Close your eyes, see it in your mind like a video and feel the emotions it brings. Write a summary here:

_____

☐ Write out or letter one godly affirmation below based on Scripture that you need to hear today. For example, I am loved.

☐ Pray for one of your weekly prayer requests. Write it here:

_____

☐ End your prayer time in gratitude, praise, and worship. Thank God for hearing your prayers and for anything else that comes to mind. Praise Him for what He has done for you and worship Him alone. As you worship, put your full focus on God and not on yourself.

Gratitude:

Praise:

Worship:

Date: _____

☐ Start with five minutes in silent meditation or with a breath prayer. See the appendix for examples.

☐ Begin with gratitude. Write out three things you are grateful for today. Be specific and include anything that happened in the last twenty-four hours.

Thank you, God, for: _____

Thank you, God, for: _____

Thank you, God, for: _____

☐ Take a moment to confess any sin from the last twenty-four hours and ask for God's forgiveness. _____

_____

_____

☐ Invite the Holy Spirit to teach you from the Scriptures today. *Holy Spirit come and open my mind so I can understand and receive what You have for me in Your Word. Reveal Yourself to me.*

☐ Bible reading. Write one takeaway from the verses you read today. If you prefer, choose a phrase that stuck out to you and write it out or letter it below.

Write out your prayers. Start off by writing everything that is currently on your heart and mind below. Pour out your heart to God (Psalms 62:8) and allow Him to clear your mind of the clutter. This will create space for you to hear God's still small voice (1 Kings 19:12) as you continue to journal on the next page.

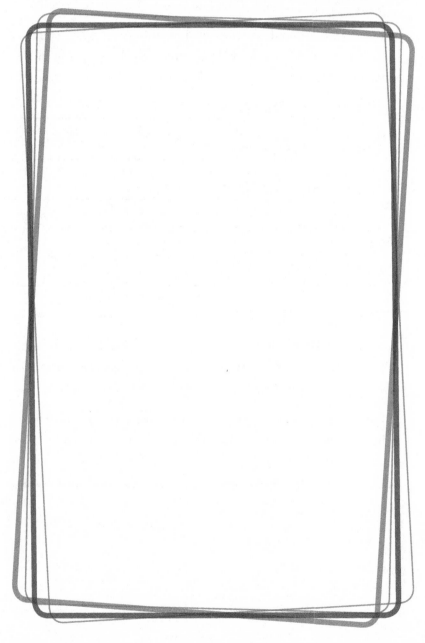

Listening prayer (two-way journaling). This is a conversation between you and God. Start off by asking an open ended question in your journal below. Then wait to hear God's voice and write what you sense Him saying to you. See the appendix for sample questions.

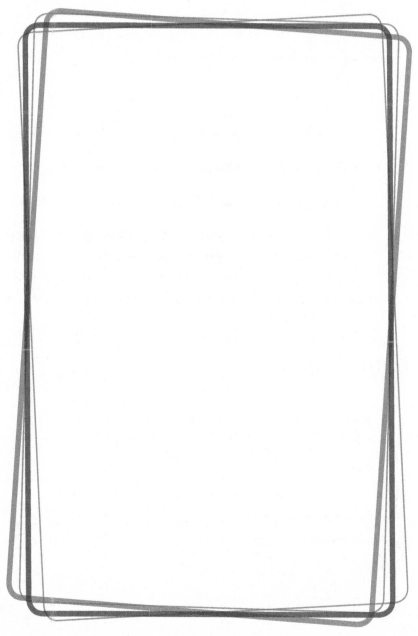

☐ Review the vision God has given you for your life, business, family, etc. Close your eyes, see it in your mind like a video and feel the emotions it brings. Write a summary here:

_____

☐ Write out or letter one godly affirmation below based on Scripture that you need to hear today. For example, I am loved.

☐ Pray for one of your weekly prayer requests. Write it here:

_____

☐ End your prayer time in gratitude, praise, and worship. Thank God for hearing your prayers and for anything else that comes to mind. Praise Him for what He has done for you and worship Him alone. As you worship, put your full focus on God and not on yourself.

Gratitude:

Praise:

Worship:

Date:_____

⟿⟞⟵

☐ Start with five minutes in silent meditation or with a breath prayer. See the appendix for examples.

☐ Begin with gratitude. Write out three things you are grateful for today. Be specific and include anything that happened in the last twenty-four hours.

Thank you, God, for:_____

Thank you, God, for:_____

Thank you, God, for:_____

☐ Take a moment to confess any sin from the last twenty-four hours and ask for God's forgiveness. _____

_____

_____

☐ Invite the Holy Spirit to teach you from the Scriptures today. *Holy Spirit come and open my mind so I can understand and receive what You have for me in Your Word. Reveal Yourself to me.*

☐ Bible reading. Write one takeaway from the verses you read today. If you prefer, choose a phrase that stuck out to you and write it out or letter it below.

Write out your prayers. Start off by writing everything that is currently on your heart and mind below. Pour out your heart to God (Psalms 62:8) and allow Him to clear your mind of the clutter. This will create space for you to hear God's still small voice (1 Kings 19:12) as you continue to journal on the next page.

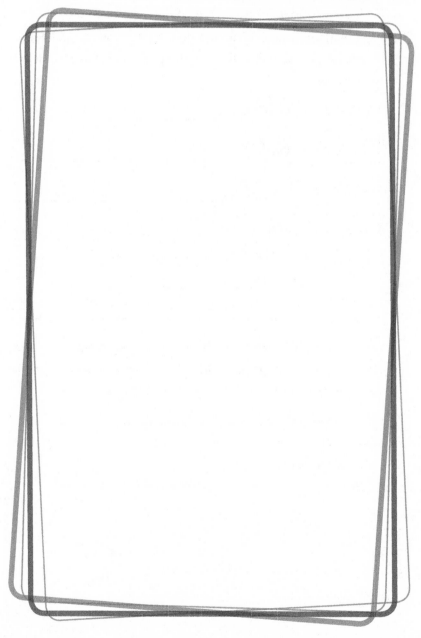

☐ Listening prayer (two-way journaling). This is a conversation between you and God. Start off by asking an open ended question in your journal below. Then wait to hear God's voice and write what you sense Him saying to you. See the appendix for sample questions.

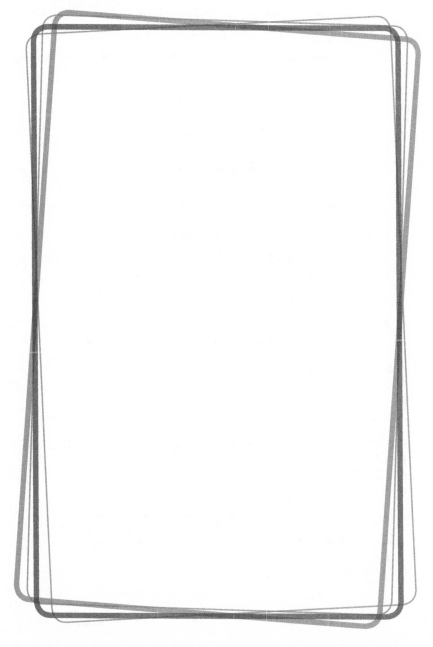

☐ Review the vision God has given you for your life, business, family, etc. Close your eyes, see it in your mind like a video and feel the emotions it brings. Write a summary here:

_____

☐ Write out or letter one godly affirmation below based on Scripture that you need to hear today. For example, I am loved.

_____

☐ Pray for one of your weekly prayer requests. Write it here:

_____

☐ End your prayer time in gratitude, praise, and worship. Thank God for hearing your prayers and for anything else that comes to mind. Praise Him for what He has done for you and worship Him alone. As you worship, put your full focus on God and not on yourself.

Gratitude:

Praise:

Worship:

Date: _____

⸎

☐ Start with five minutes in silent meditation or with a breath prayer. See the appendix for examples.

☐ Begin with gratitude. Write out three things you are grateful for today. Be specific and include anything that happened in the last twenty-four hours.

Thank you, God, for: _____

Thank you, God, for: _____

Thank you, God, for: _____

☐ Take a moment to confess any sin from the last twenty-four hours and ask for God's forgiveness. _____

_____

_____

☐ Invite the Holy Spirit to teach you from the Scriptures today. *Holy Spirit come and open my mind so I can understand and receive what You have for me in Your Word. Reveal Yourself to me.*

☐ Bible reading. Write one takeaway from the verses you read today. If you prefer, choose a phrase that stuck out to you and write it out or letter it below.

Write out your prayers. Start off by writing everything that is currently on your heart and mind below. Pour out your heart to God (Psalms 62:8) and allow Him to clear your mind of the clutter. This will create space for you to hear God's still small voice (1 Kings 19:12) as you continue to journal on the next page.

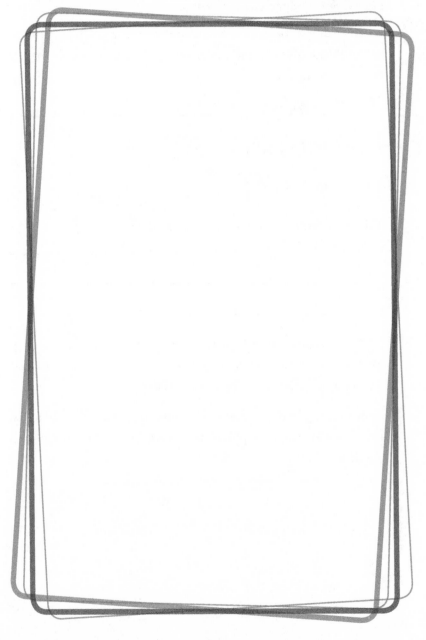

Listening prayer (two-way journaling). This is a conversation between you and God. Start off by asking an open ended question in your journal below. Then wait to hear God's voice and write what you sense Him saying to you. See the appendix for sample questions.

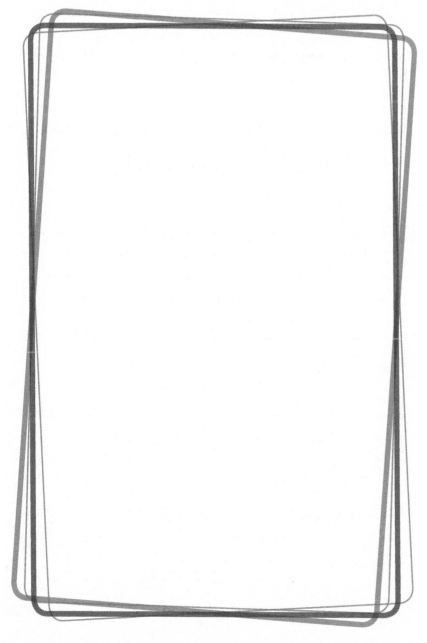

☐ Review the vision God has given you for your life, business, family, etc. Close your eyes, see it in your mind like a video and feel the emotions it brings. Write a summary here:

_____

☐ Write out or letter one godly affirmation below based on Scripture that you need to hear today. For example, I am loved.

☐ Pray for one of your weekly prayer requests. Write it here:

_____

☐ End your prayer time in gratitude, praise, and worship. Thank God for hearing your prayers and for anything else that comes to mind. Praise Him for what He has done for you and worship Him alone. As you worship, put your full focus on God and not on yourself.

Gratitude:

Praise:

Worship:

Date: _____

☐ Start with five minutes in silent meditation or with a breath prayer. See the appendix for examples.

☐ Begin with gratitude. Write out three things you are grateful for today. Be specific and include anything that happened in the last twenty-four hours.

Thank you, God, for: _____

Thank you, God, for: _____

Thank you, God, for: _____

☐ Take a moment to confess any sin from the last twenty-four hours and ask for God's forgiveness. _____

_____

_____

☐ Invite the Holy Spirit to teach you from the Scriptures today. *Holy Spirit come and open my mind so I can understand and receive what You have for me in Your Word. Reveal Yourself to me.*

☐ Bible reading. Write one takeaway from the verses you read today. If you prefer, choose a phrase that stuck out to you and write it out or letter it below.

Write out your prayers. Start off by writing everything that is currently on your heart and mind below. Pour out your heart to God (Psalms 62:8) and allow Him to clear your mind of the clutter. This will create space for you to hear God's still small voice (1 Kings 19:12) as you continue to journal on the next page.

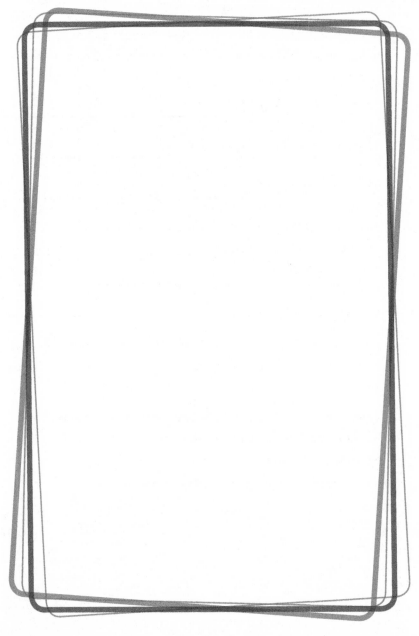

☐ Listening prayer (two-way journaling). This is a conversation between you and God. Start off by asking an open ended question in your journal below. Then wait to hear God's voice and write what you sense Him saying to you. See the appendix for sample questions.

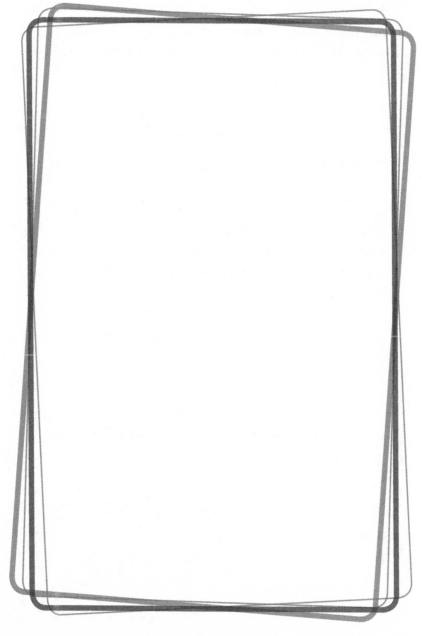

☐ Review the vision God has given you for your life, business, family, etc. Close your eyes, see it in your mind like a video and feel the emotions it brings. Write a summary here:

_____

☐ Write out or letter one godly affirmation below based on Scripture that you need to hear today. For example, I am loved.

☐ Pray for one of your weekly prayer requests. Write it here:

_____

☐ End your prayer time in gratitude, praise, and worship. Thank God for hearing your prayers and for anything else that comes to mind. Praise Him for what He has done for you and worship Him alone. As you worship, put your full focus on God and not on yourself.

Gratitude:

Praise:

Worship:

Date: _____

☐ Start with five minutes in silent meditation or with a breath prayer. See the appendix for examples.

☐ Begin with gratitude. Write out three things you are grateful for today. Be specific and include anything that happened in the last twenty-four hours.

Thank you, God, for: _____

Thank you, God, for: _____

Thank you, God, for: _____

☐ Take a moment to confess any sin from the last twenty-four hours and ask for God's forgiveness. _____

_____

_____

☐ Invite the Holy Spirit to teach you from the Scriptures today. *Holy Spirit come and open my mind so I can understand and receive what You have for me in Your Word. Reveal Yourself to me.*

☐ Bible reading. Write one takeaway from the verses you read today. If you prefer, choose a phrase that stuck out to you and write it out or letter it below.

Write out your prayers. Start off by writing everything that is currently on your heart and mind below. Pour out your heart to God (Psalms 62:8) and allow Him to clear your mind of the clutter. This will create space for you to hear God's still small voice (1 Kings 19:12) as you continue to journal on the next page.

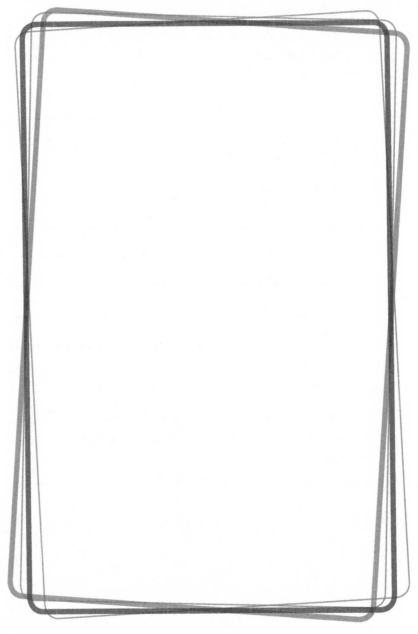

☐ Listening prayer (two-way journaling). This is a conversation between you and God. Start off by asking an open ended question in your journal below. Then wait to hear God's voice and write what you sense Him saying to you. See the appendix for sample questions.

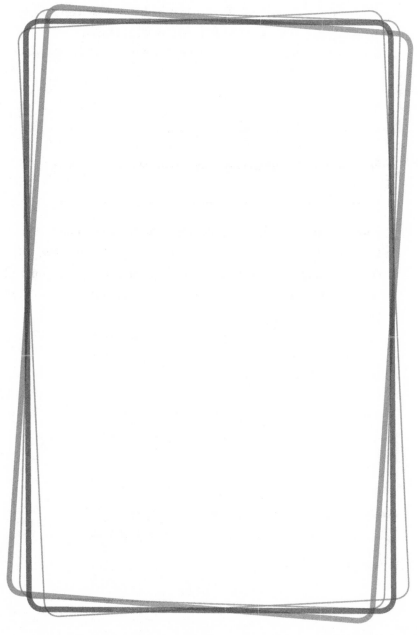

☐ Review the vision God has given you for your life, business, family, etc. Close your eyes, see it in your mind like a video and feel the emotions it brings. Write a summary here:

_____

☐ Write out or letter one godly affirmation below based on Scripture that you need to hear today. For example, I am loved.

☐ Pray for one of your weekly prayer requests. Write it here:

_____

☐ End your prayer time in gratitude, praise, and worship. Thank God for hearing your prayers and for anything else that comes to mind. Praise Him for what He has done for you and worship Him alone. As you worship, put your full focus on God and not on yourself.

Gratitude:

Praise:

Worship:

Extra Journaling Pages

This section contains extra journaling pages. Some days you may have more to write about and so we've created these overflow pages for you.

Simply write at the bottom of your daily journaling page, continued on page ____ and write the page number for the overflow page you used.

Put the date at the top of the overflow page and continue your journaling.

Enjoy!

Date: _____

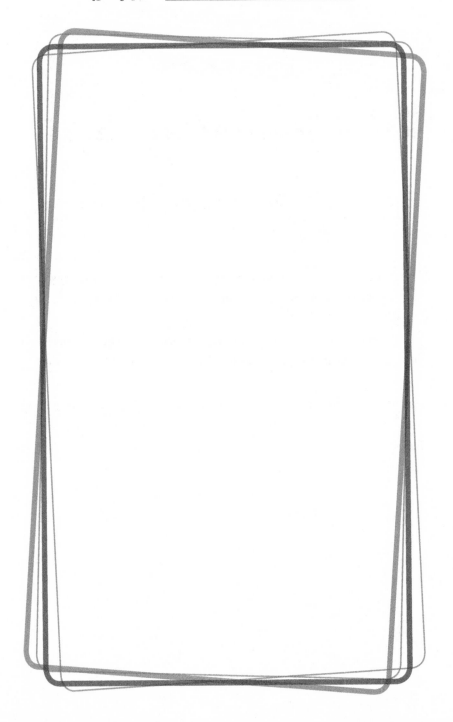

Date: _____

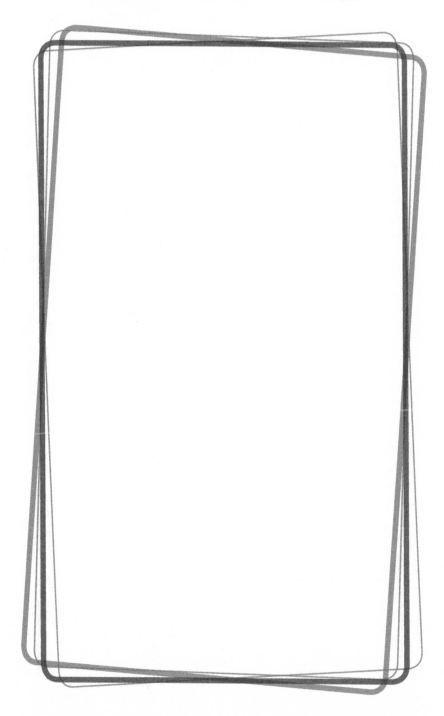

Date: _____

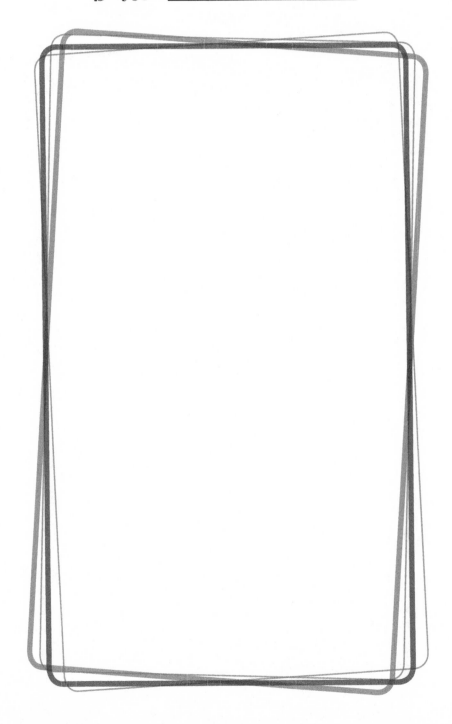

Date: _____

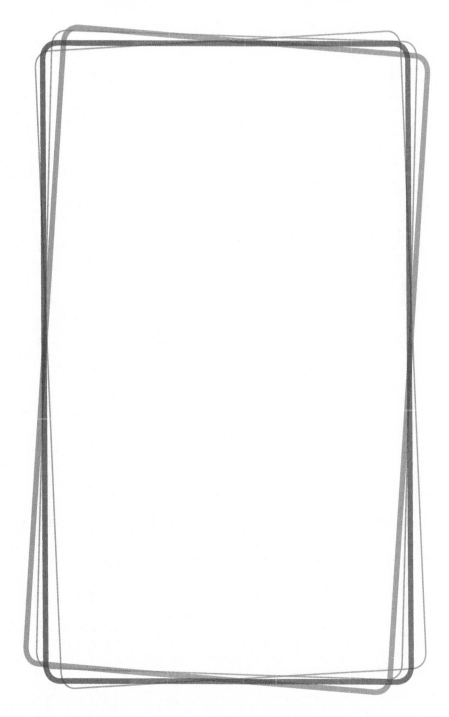

Date: _____

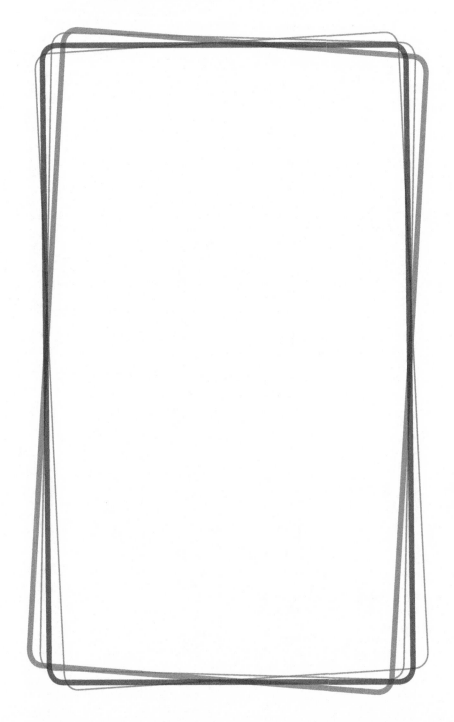

Date:_____

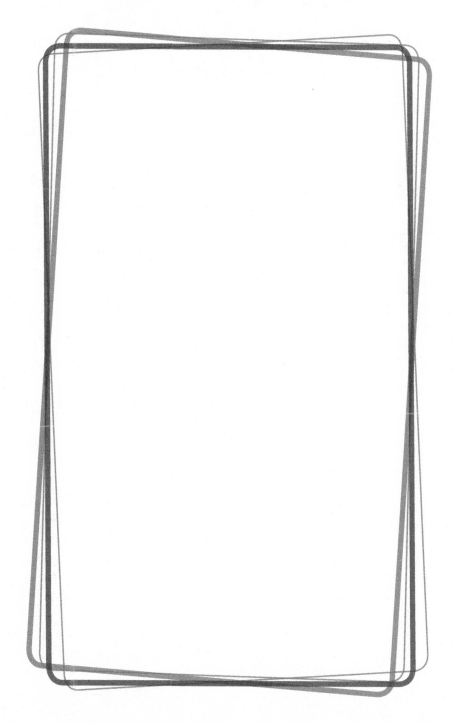

Date: _____

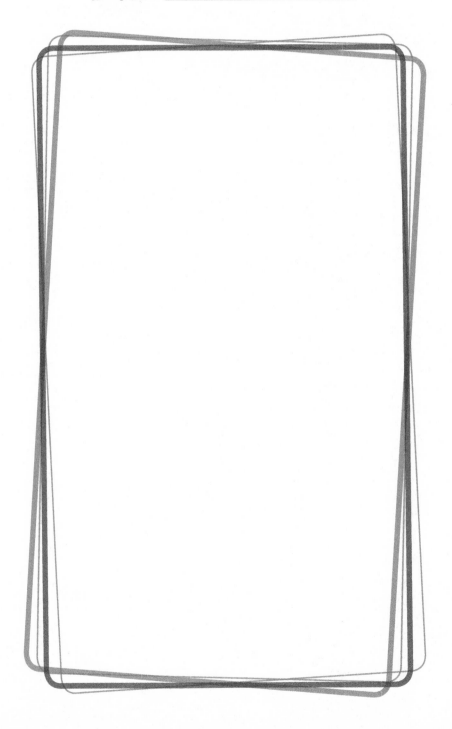

Date: _____

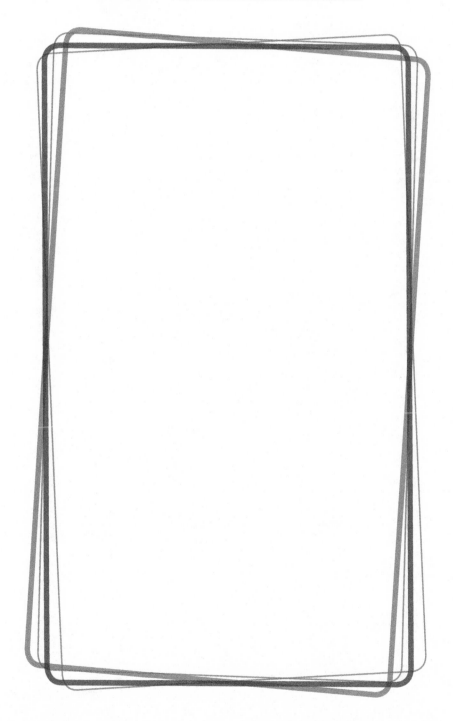

Date: _____

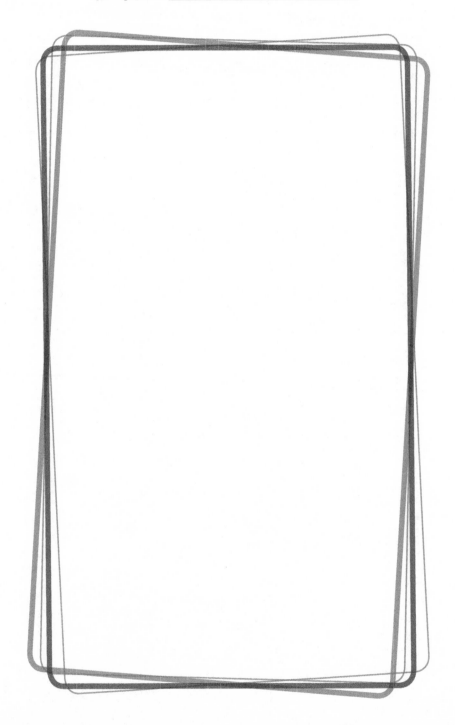

Date: _____

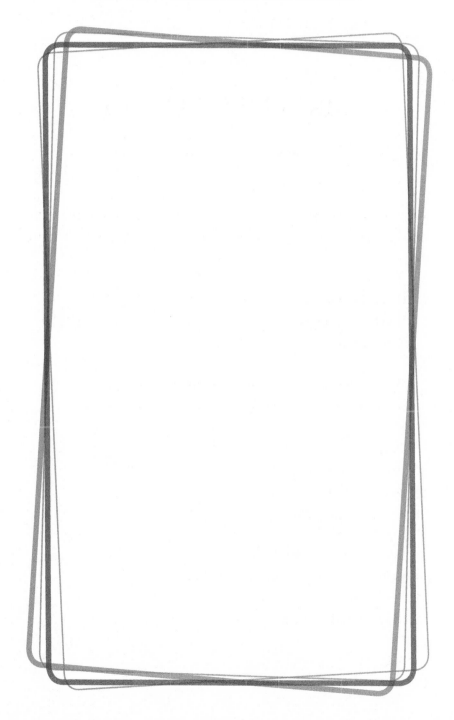

BREATH PRAYERS

This is not an extensive list of breath prayers, but is a starting point for you. You can use these prayers during the time of silent meditation each day.

1. Come, Lord Jesus.
2. Holy Spirit, Come.
3. Peace, be still.
4. Lord, have mercy.
5. Speak, Lord, for your servant is listening.
6. My help comes from the Lord, maker of heaven and earth.
7. Here I am.
8. Show Your power.
9. When I am afraid, I will trust You.
10. Not my will, but Yours.
11. Bring Your kingdom.
12. Say the word.
13. Be still and know that I am God.
14. Help me understand Your ways, Lord.
15. Lord I am Yours.
16. My Lord and my God.
17. Peace.
18. Faith.
19. Come.

20. Love.
21. Abba.
22. Immanuel.
23. Gracious Lord.
24. Only You, Lord.
25. O Lord, show me Your way.
26. Holy One, heal me.
27. Abide in me, Lord.
28. My God and my all.
29. My Jesus, mercy.
30. Abba, I belong to You.
31. I belong to You, O Lord.
32. My soul, bless the Lord.
33. Open my heart to Your love.
34. Lord, I give myself to You.
35. Lord, increase my faith.
36. Thy kingdom come, Thy will be done.
37. Jesus, my light and my love.
38. May all of my being praise You, Lord.
39. Holy Spirit, pray in me.
40. Lord, do with me what You will.
41. I am God's beloved child.
42. Create in me a clean heart.
43. You, Lord, are always with me.
44. Selah.
45. The Lord is my Shepherd. I shall not want.
46. Jesus, come into my heart.
47. More of You, less of me.
48. Let me know Your peace, O God.
49. Teach me patience, gracious God.
50. Let me feel Your love, Lord.
51. Help me, Father.
52. Resting in You, Lord.
53. Direct my heart, dear Lord.

54. Strengthen me, Jesus.
55. I exalt You, Lord.
56. You are God.

LIST OF QUESTIONS TO USE IN LISTENING PRAYER

Start off asking God an open ended question in your journal. Use one of the following questions to get started.

- Lord, what do You have for me today?
- What do You want to say to me today?
- How do You see me?
- What season is it for me right now?
- What happened to my heart yesterday?
- What am I running from?
- What am I striving for?
- Where am I living in scarcity, poverty or lack?
- What do I need to know? What do I need to try?
- What do I need to accept?
- What do I need to do (or what should I do next)?
- Sometimes, in order to receive, we need to release something. Lord, what do I need to release today?
- What's NOT working?
- What's holding me back right now?

Note: If this is a new concept to you, watch the bonus training here: www.yourcreativeadventure.com/illuminatebonus

GODLY AFFIRMATIONS

This is not an extensive list of godly affirmations, but is a starting point for you. We encourage you to also come up with your own godly affirmations based on Scripture for what you need reminded of right now. There is a place in your journal each day to write out one godly affirmation.

I AM LOVED

- I am loved with an unfailing love (Psalm 5:7, 13:5, 23:6, 26:3, 31:7, 42:8).
- I am surrounded with a shield of love (Psalm 5:12).
- The faithful love of the Lord for me never ends (Lamentations 3:22).
- Because I love Jesus, the Father loves me (John 14:23).
- Nothing in heaven or on earth can separate me from God's love (Romans 8:38-39).
- Jesus loves me and gave himself for me (Galatians 2:20).
- My roots grow down into God's love (Ephesians 3:17).
- I experience the love of Christ daily (Ephesians 3:19).
- I am filled with faith and love (1 Timothy 1:14).
- Perfect love casts out fear (1 John 4:18).

I AM SECURE AND SAFE

- I am a member of Christ's body (1 Corinthians 12:27, Ephesians 5:30).
- I am a saint (Ephesians 1:1, 1 Corinthians 1:2, Philippians 1:1, Colossians 1:2).
- I am a citizen of heaven (Philippians 3:20; Ephesians 2:6).
- I am hidden with Christ in God (Colossians 3:3).
- I am one of God's living stones, being built up in Christ (1 Peter 2:5).
- I am born of God and the devil cannot touch me (1 John 5:18).
- God's right hand holds me securely (Psalm 63:8).
- Because I trust in the Lord, I am secure (Psalm 125:1).
- Because I fear the Lord, I am secure (Proverbs 14:26).
- The Lord watches over me when I'm sleeping (Psalm 3:5, 4:8).
- The Lord is my refuge and place of safety (Psalm 18:2).
- The Lord keeps me safe from my enemies (Psalm 18:48).
- I live safely beneath the shelter of your wings (Psalm 61:4).
- God alone is my place of safety (Psalm 91:2).
- I run to the Lord for safety (Proverbs 18:10).
- Christ is bringing me safely home to God (1 Peter 3:18).
- I am safe in the care of Jesus (Jude 1:1).

I AM CHOSEN AND AN HEIR

- I am a child of God (John 1:12).
- I am a friend of Jesus (John 15:15).
- I am chosen and appointed by Jesus to bear fruit (John 15:16).
- I am a joint heir with Christ (Romans 8:17).
- I am a son/daughter of God (Romans 8:14-15, Galatians 3:26, 4:6).
- I am chosen of God, holy and dearly loved (Colossians 3:12, 1 Thessalonians 1:4).

I AM FREE

- Christ has truly set me free (Galatians 5:1).
- I walk in total freedom (Psalm 119:45).
- I live in the freedom of God's grace (Romans 6:14).
- Because the Spirit of the Lord lives in me, I live in freedom (2 Corinthians 3:17).
- I am adopted by God and live in freedom (Galatians 4:5).
- I enjoy the freedom Jesus purchased for me (Ephesians 1:7, Colossians 1:14, 1 Tim. 2:6).
- God frees me from my fears (Psalm 34:4).
- God has set me free (Psalm 118:5).
- I was a captive that God set free (Isaiah 42:7, 61:1, Luke 4:18).
- The Truth of God sets me free (John 8:32).
- The Son has set me free (John 8:36).
- I have been set free from the power of sin (Romans 6:7).
- I am free from all blame (1 Corinthians 1:8).
- I am free from all spiritual powers of this world (Colossians 2:20).
- I am free from every kind of sin (Titus 2:14).

NAMES OF GOD

This is not an extensive list of the names of God, but is a starting point for you. These are names you can use during your time of worship in your journal each day.

1. **Elohim:** God (Genesis 1:1), root = Alah - to swear, or to bind with oath. Meaning = strong creator.
2. **Jehovah:** Lord (Genesis 2:4), root = Hayah - to become, or to continue to be. Meaning = self-existent one who reveals Himself.
3. **Adonai:** Lord (Genesis 15:2), root = to be master. Meaning = the master of a slave.
4. **Jehovah Roi:** The Lord is my Shepherd (Genesis 48:15, Psalm 23:1). He leads by example, feeds us by leading us to green pastures and protects us.
5. **Jehovah Jireh:** The Lord shall provide (Genesis 22:14). Life's basic needs are provided by Jehovah Jireh. Jesus Christ was the ultimate provision of Jehovah Jireh, the God who supplies both our physical and spiritual needs.
6. **Jehovah Shalom:** The Lord our peace (Judges 6:24). The Lord takes care of us in times of discouragement and in the emotional storms of life.
7. **Jehovah Rapha:** The Lord our Healer (Exodus 15:26). Preventative and corrective healing. He is able to heal us and brings us to wholeness physically, spiritually, emotionally, and mentally.

ATTRIBUTES OF GOD

"But the people who know their God will display strength and take action."
Daniel 11:32, NASB

This is not an extensive list of the attibutes of God, but is a starting point for you. These are attibutes you can use during your time of worship in your journal each day.

NATURAL ATTRIBUTES
They relate to God inwardly as He is in himself.

1. **Omniscient:** Knows everything (Psalm 139:1-6, Psalm 147:5, Hebrews 4:13).
2. **Omnipotent:** Possesses all power (Genesis 18:14, Job 42:2, Jeremiah 32:17&27).
3. **Omnipresent:** Present everywhere at all times (Proverbs 15:33, Jeremiah 23:23-24).
4. **Eternal:** No beginning, no end, not confined to time (Deuteronomy 32:40, Isaiah 52:15).
5. **Immutable:** God never changes (Psalm 102:25-27, Malachi 3:6, Hebrews 13:6, James 1:17).
6. **Incomprehensible:** Beyond our understanding (Job 11:7, Romans 11:33).

7. **Self-Existent:** Depends on nothing for His existence (Exodus 3:14, John 5:26, also see the name Jehovah, self-existent one).

8. **Self-Sufficient:** Brings about His will without any help (Psalm 139:1-6, Psalm 147:5, Hebrews 4:13).

9. **Infinite:** No limits or bounds whatsoever (1 Kings 8:27, Psalm 145:3).

10. **Transcendent:** Above creation, exists totally apart from His creation (Isaiah 43:10, Isaiah 55:8-9).

11. **Sovereign:** In total control and is totally supreme (Daniel 4:35).

MORAL ATTRIBUTES

They reveal God outwardly to His creation.

12. **Holy:** Morally excellent, perfect (Leviticus 19:2, Job 34:10, Isaiah 47:4, Isaiah 57:15).

13. **Righteous:** Always does right (Deuteronomy 32:4, Psalm 119:142)

14. **Just:** Fair in all His actions (Numbers 14:18, Numbers 23:19, Psalm 89:14).

15. **Merciful:** loving kindness, compassion, exhibits active compassion against those who offend Him (Psalm 62:12, Psalm 89:14, Psalm 106:44-45, Psalm 116:5, Romans 9:14-16).

16. **Long Suffering:** Righteous anger is slow to be kindled (Numbers 14:18, 2 Peter 3:9).

17. **Wise:** His understanding is unfathomable, it causes Him to choose righteous ends (Isaiah 40:28, Daniel 2:20).

18. **Loving:** Exhibits a love not based on worth or merit of the object of His love. He loves with an everlasting love. (Jeremiah 31:3, Romans 5:8, 1 John 4:8).

19. **Good:** God is good and gives according to His good will and not according to what we deserve (2 Chronicles 5:13, Psalm 106:44-48, Psalm 5:1, Psalm 106:1).

20. **Wrathful:** Hatred for all unrighteousness (Exodus 34:6-7, 2 Chronicles 19:2, Romans 1:18).

21. **Truthful:** Whatever God speaks is truth (Numbers 23:19, Psalm 31:5, Titus 1:2).

22. **Faithful:** Always true to His promises. God keeps His covenant (Deuteronomy 7:9, 2 Timothy 2:13).

23. **Jealous:** Unwilling to share what is rightfully His (Exodus 20:5, Exodus 34:14).

RESOURCES

Book Bonuses: Access all the book bonuses including a workshop on how to hear the voice of God ($69 value) here: www.yourcreativeadventure.com/illuminatebonus

Free Art of Prayer eBook: A 6-day devotional guide that will help you to add color and creativity to your prayer life. Download here: http://yourcreativeadventure.com/artofprayer

Illuminate Podcast - Join CJ and Shelley to dig deeper into God's Word and listen for FREE here: http://illuminateshow.com

Your Creative Adventure podcast for Christian artists and writers: Are you an artist? Listen to CJ and Shelley's podcast here: http://yourcreativeadventure.com/subscribe

Additional Books by Shelley Hitz:

Broken Crayons Still Color
Calligraphy for Beginners
Brush Strokes Workbook

Made in the USA
Coppell, TX
11 December 2022

88623581R00111